BOOK AND LIBRARY PLAYS

For Elementary and High School Use

BOOK AND LIBRARY PLAYS

PLAYS

For Elementary and High School Use

Selected and Edited by

EDITH M. PHELPS

Volume II

THE H. W. WILSON COMPANY
NEW YORK 1941

PRINTED IN THE UNITED STATES OF AMERICA

PREFACE

The cordial reception accorded *Book and Library Plays* which appeared in 1938, has been an encouragement to collect for publication a second group of these amateur plays. From the many received in response to the invitation extended in the *Wilson Library Bulletin,* seventeen have been selected, of varying length and degree of difficulty, so as to meet the needs of both grade and high school students. Librarians, teachers, and often the students themselves, contributed to the making of these plays. It is to be hoped that those who use them will have as much fun in presenting them as the originators had in preparing and producing them. They will be helpful in programs for Book Week celebrations, for assembly or class use, parent teacher meetings, or for any occasion where the gospel of books and the library can be spread.

July 15, 1941

EDITH M. PHELPS

Contents

Sherlock Holmes and the Gorgon's Head

by

Margaret Paulus

A Book Week Playlet for Boys

Presented As an Assembly Program at the Technical
High School, Milwaukee, Wis.

Characters:
> John
> Ken
> Sherlock Holmes
> Doctor Watson
> Several Students

Scene:

The action of this play for boys can be adapted to local school library conditions by any slight necessary changes in the directions which the monitor gives for charging books, the names of the encyclopedias used, and so on. The use of the actual names of the boys playing the student parts is probably more effective than the use of fictitious names.

The scene is the library. A minimum of scenery and properties will serve. This playlet, in fact, can be presented in the classroom or in the library itself. A dictionary stand and an unabridged dictionary are at stage right, a table and chair serve as the charging desk at upper right. A book stack marked prominently, *Reference,* stands at left with another small table and a chair in front of it. A book stack marked *Fiction* stands at center back. This stack is intended to conceal the characters of Sherlock Holmes and Doctor Watson, who enter and exit from here. It might be advisable to hang a curtain or sheets of heavy wrapping paper at the rear of the shelves so as to assure these characters being concealed from the audience until the time of their entrance.

The stacks may be filled with regular library copies, or with dummy books for all but the few which the action of the play requires to be taken from the shelves. If there are any large, badly-worn books available which can be marked very prominently on the backs so that the audience can see the volume numbers and letters as they are refered to on the stage, these would be excellent to use for the encyclopedias.

No royalty charged for production

Sherlock Holmes and the Gorgon's Head

[*At the rise of the curtain, or—lacking a curtain to rise—simply at the beginning of the play, we find ourselves in the midst of the three-fifteen rush at the close of the school day. John, the library monitor, is attempting to work rapidly and efficiently at the charging desk, but the group of five or six clustered about the desk is making matters very difficult. They are all speaking at once and we hear only snatches of intelligible conversation*]

STUDENT 1: Hey, going to the game Saturday?

STUDENT 2: You can't tell me that girl was your sister. Why she's good looking.

STUDENT 3: What page was the English assignment?

STUDENT 4: So I went right up to him and I said, "Forty-four problems are too many."

STUDENT 5: Len'me a pencil, somebody.

[*These remarks can be distinguished in the general hubhub. The voice of Ken, who is on the edge of the group, and is trying to attract John's attention can be heard persistently*]

KEN: Hey, where can I find—Listen, John, where is—Have you anything about—Say, listen a minute—

JOHN: [*leaping to his feet and tapping on the table with his pencil until the others calm down*] Listen, you fellows, I'm just as anxious to get out of here as you are. I've got to get to student council meeting. And if you

11

mugs won't pipe down and get in line and be a little more orderly we'll never get these books charged. Now please get in line where you belong and keep quiet.

[*Several of the group say "Okay" and form in a rather disorderly line. Ken takes this opportunity to get to the desk*]

KEN: John, have you any—

JOHN: Get in line with the others, Ken. I'll take you in your own turn.

KEN: But look. All I want is for you to answer one question. Just a very simple question. That's all I want. If you'll just give me a chance to—

JOHN: All right. Hurry up. What's the question?

KEN: Where can I find about—about a—about—now wait—[*Searches through his pockets for notebook, finally locates it and leafs it through, looking for notation, while the rest of the line fidgets and grumbles impatiently*] Now wait a second. I have it right here some place. It's—no—here it is—no, it isn't.

STUDENT IN LINE: Hurry up, will you, Ken?

KEN: Got it. Where can I find out about Medusa?

JOHN: About what?

KEN: Medusa.

JOHN: Look in the catalog.

KEN: I did, and it isn't there.

JOHN: Look in the encyclopedia.

KEN: [*bitterly triumphant*] I did, and it isn't there either. At least it doesn't tell anything.

JOHN: Well, maybe—

FIRST BOY IN LINE: John, will you check out this book for me, please? I have to get to my corner to sell papers and I can't wait all night.

JOHN: Okay. Sorry, Ken. I don't know what to tell you. Miss Smith's at a faculty meeting—

12

KEN: Yeah. She *would* be. Just when I gotta find out something.

JOHN: Better try the catalog again. Maybe you skipped right over the card. And it seems to me there must be something in the encyclopedia.

[*Ken goes to the reference shelves gloomily. While the other boys are checking out books he stands glaring at the encyclopedias and running an aimless finger across their backs*]

JOHN: [*checking books*] What's this name? Alfred Sartz? Partz? What is it?

BOY IN LINE: Hartz. That's an H.

JOHN: Well, write it more plainly, please. The idea in having you sign your name is so we know who has the book. Nobody could tell from that. [*As first boy rewrites name, John continues to check out books for others in line*] Remember this book with the pink card is due tomorrow morning at 8:30.

BOY IN LINE: Yes, I'll remember.

JOHN: [*to next boy in line*] You'll have to put one of these back. Only one fiction book may be borrowed at a time.

FOURTH BOY IN LINE: May I renew these?

JOHN: [*after consulting file*] You may renew this one. But the other has been renewed once for you. You can't renew a book twice.

FOURTH BOY: But I need this for chemistry class.

JOHN: Sorry, but maybe some other student needs it too. Give somebody else a chance at it. [*to the last boy in the line who is returning a book*] This is a day overdue. You owe us a cent.

LAST BOY: [*parting with his cent reluctantly*] This is where all my money goes. I think I'll stop getting books from this library.

13

JOHN: Why don't you try bringing them back on time?

LAST BOY: I'll try, but it doesn't seem to do me much good. I just never remember that my books are due.

JOHN: If I were you I'd just cheat the library out of those overdue fines and get the books back when they should be back.

[*The boys leave. John glances hastily at his watch and prepares to leave. He speaks to Ken, still sadly contemplating the backs of the encyclopedias as if he expected knowledge to spring upon him*]

JOHN: Are you going to be here for a little while, Ken?

KEN: [*sulkily*] I guess so. I can't find anything I want.

JOHN: Miss Smith will be back in a few minutes and I have to get to my student council meeting. If anyone comes in will you tell him to wait and Miss Smith will be back?

KEN: Sure. I have to wait to see Miss Smith myself. I have to find out about this dopey Medusa.

JOHN: What is Medusa?

KEN: How should I know? That's what I'm trying to find out.

JOHN: Well, sorry I couldn't be of more help. And thanks for looking after things here. So long!

KEN: So long! [*walks about stage muttering*] Dumb old assignment anyway. Who ever heard of the dumb old Medusa? I think teachers sit up nights thinking up these dumb old assignments. [*Stops in front of fiction shelves*] Dumb old dopey books they have here. Nothing exciting like Doc Savage or Tarzan. No detective stories. [*Suddenly leans closer to shelf*] Huh! Adventures of Sherlock Holmes. Why he was a detective. I saw him in the movies! [*Takes book from shelf and leafs through it*] Yup! This is the one! Here's Doctor Watson! [*reading table of contents*] A Case of Identity! The Adventure of the Speckled Band!

14

[*greatly astonished*] Well, what do you know! Detective stories in school! [*Keeping his eyes on the book, he sits down on the floor, leans comfortably against the bookshelves, draws his knees up and rests the book on them, and begins to read very intently. He reads aloud at first so that his words are heard by the audience, but they soon trail off into an unintelligible murmur*]

KEN: [*reading*] " 'Holmes', said I, as I stood one morning in our bow-window looking down the street, 'here is a madman coming along. It seems rather sad that his relatives should allow him to come out alone.' My friend rose lazily—"

[*While Ken is intent on his reading* SHERLOCK HOLMES *and* DOCTOR WATSON *step out from behind the book stack and regard him thoughtfully. Holmes should be equipped with his usual cap and a magnifying glass through which he peers down at Ken*]

WATSON: [*to Holmes*] That boy would make a great detective, Holmes. Marvelous powers of concentration.

HOLMES: Yes. But have you noticed how he concentrates on the wrong things, Watson? Now if he had given the same attention to his own investigation that he is giving to mine he'd have his mystery solved by now.

KEN: [*closing the book*] Say, that was swell the way he— [*Notices Holmes and Watson for the first time and scrambles to feet*] Where did you come from? Who are you?

HOLMES: Allow me to present myself, Sherlock Holmes, and my very good friend and biographer, Doctor Watson.

KEN: How do you—Sherlock Holmes! Why I thought—I mean—uh, excuse me—I didn't know you were a real person.

WATSON: A real person! Why how could Holmes be anything but real? Think of all the hundreds and thou-

15

sands of people who are friends and admirers of Sherlock Holmes.

KEN: We—ell, of course, now I see that you're real. Even so I thought after all these years you must be—I mean, I thought you'd be older or—or—

HOLMES: [*dryly*]—or dead. Yes, quite. One would think so.

WATSON: Holmes grow older or die! How utterly preposterous! How could he when boys like you—and thousands of other boys still to come—keep on meeting and admiring him. Holmes couldn't grow old.

KEN: No, I suppose you're right. You know, Mr. Holmes, I'd like just awfully well to be a detective.

HOLMES: Do you think you'd be a good detective?

KEN: I hope so. I could be, I guess, if only I had enough clues to work on.

HOLMES: The trouble with most people who try to be detectives is that they don't recognize a clue when they see one.

KEN: Oh, I wouldn't do that.

HOLMES: Or they don't know where to look for clues.

KEN: That's easy. At the scene of the crime.

HOLMES: Suppose you don't know the scene of the crime?

KEN: I don't know. That would be tough, wouldn't it?

WATSON: [*proudly*] Not for Holmes.

KEN: No, I suppose not. But it certainly would be for me. Sherlock—I mean—Mr. Holmes, I wish you'd tell me something about how you go about solving your mysteries.

HOLMES: It's all in the books, Ken. My good friends, Doctor Watson and Sir Arthur Conan Doyle, have seen to that.

KEN: Yes, but I'd like to actually see you in action.

HOLMES: Very well. Have you a mystery that needs solving?

16

KEN: No. Nothing mysterious ever happens around here.

HOLMES: I thought I heard you talking about not being able to find something.

KEN: Me? Oh, you mean that about Medusa? But that's no mystery. That's just a dumb English assignment.

HOLMES: Quite on the contrary, Ken. It sounds to me like a first class mystery. Nothing in the catalog, nothing in the encyclopedia, not a single clue. Just the type of case we like, eh, Watson?

WATSON: [*pompously*] Yes, indeed, Holmes. A very interesting case.

HOLMES: Now in the first place let's see what clues we have. What are we looking for? What is this Medusa?

KEN: That's just it. I haven't any idea what it is.

HOLMES: Then our course is obvious. We go to our best source of information on the meaning of words. We consult the dictionary.

KEN: [*delighted to find that even the great Sherlock Holmes can be wrong*] I thought of that, and it isn't in the dictionary—[*yanking a very small and very battered pocket dictionary from his jacket pocket*] See. Here are the M's. Medal—medicine—meditate—meek —meet—nothing like Medusa.

HOLMES: Very likely not, my dear fellow. What did you expect? That little book is all very well for a pocket companion. Indeed, I'm pleased to see you carry it. But when you have a really elusive quarry like the word Medusa to pursue you need stronger weapons than that. Now there [*pointing toward the unabridged dictionary on its stand*] that, of course, is what I meant by the dictionary.

KEN: Oh, that. [*going toward the dictionary stand reluctantly*] I never can find anything in that. It's so hard to use.

HOLMES: Why do you say that?

KEN: Well, it's so big. And I have to go over pages and pages to find anything.

HOLMES: Why? Don't you know the alphabet?

KEN: [*indignantly*] Of course I do.

HOLMES: Then there's only one reason for your difficulty. Exactly as I said, you're not recognizing clues when you see them.

KEN: Clues! What do you mean?

HOLMES: The first clue I see to using the dictionary is these little thumb indentions at the sides of the pages. [*Peers at them through his magnifying glass, then hands the glass to Ken who looks through it uncertainly*] Surely, you know what those are for.

KEN: To help turn the pages.

HOLMES: Yes. You're not entirely wrong. But why do they have the letters on them?

KEN: Letters? Oh, yes. They have, haven't they? Well —that's so—that's to—of course. It's so you can turn to the right place in the book. It's like an index. Am I dumb!

HOLMES: No, Ken. You're just like a great many other people. Simply unobservant.

WATSON: That's really why Holmes is such a great detective. His marvelous powers of observation.

HOLMES: Nonsense, Watson. We all have the same powers of observation. We don't all use the powers we have, that's all.

KEN: [*Locates M on thumb index*] Here's M. Now let me see. Macaranga! What do you suppose that is? [*turning page*] Mac Duff—machinist.

HOLMES: My dear fellow, you're ignoring clues again.

KEN: Really? Where?

HOLMES: Don't you see the guide words at the top of the page?

KEN: Guide words? These up here? Macrochina—boy, what a word! Mad—Madrogue—there's another word nobody ever heard of.

HOLMES: Don't you see, Ken? Those words indicate the first and last words to be found on the page? Now, Medusa, wouldn't come between either of those words would it?

KEN: No—[*turning pages rapidly*] no, nor here, nor here, nor—but here—Mediterranean—meet! Medusa ought to be between those two some place [*drawing a finger down the columns*] Let's see—let's see. Say—here it is! And look, a picture and everything.

HOLMES: Certainly. Certainly. So now you know what the Medusa is. Or will when you've read that.

WATSON: Marvelous, Holmes. Wonderful deduction.

HOLMES: Elementary, my dear Watson, elementary.

KEN: [*reading eagerly*] "One of the Gorgons (see Gorgon, n. 1)"—Now, what on earth does that mean?—"She was slain by Perseus"—I wonder who he was—"who succeeded in cutting off her head by looking at its reflection in his shield."—That doesn't seem to make much sense—"He gave the head to Athena, who set it in her shield. She is fabled by some to have been a beautiful maiden, whose hair was transformed into snakes by Athena, whose sanctuary she had violated." [*in a very disappointed tone*] I suppose that's something, but it won't satisfy Mr. Harris. He'll ask me to explain all about who was Perseus and who was Athena and a whole lot more I don't understand from this.

HOLMES: I see a splendid clue there to help you find out more.

KEN: Another clue? [*staring at the book and then shaking his head*] Well, I don't.

HOLMES: How about that "see Gorgon, n. 1"?

KEN: Is that a clue? What does that mean?

19

HOLMES: Naturally it means to turn to the word Gorgon and the first noun-meaning under Gorgon. "N" means noun, naturally.

KEN: Oh, naturally.

HOLMES: So, my dear fellow, we will find further information about the Medusa if we turn to Gorgon.

KEN: Well, here goes. [*using the thumb index*] Here's G and here's Gorge—Gossampine at the top of the page. It must be here some place. Here's Gorgon. Say, I never found a word that fast before.

HOLMES: Simply a matter of observing the clues.

KEN: And here's n. 1. [*reading*] "One of three fabled sisters, Stheno, Eurayle,"—they certainly had names—"and Medusa"—that's our friend—"with snaky hair and of terrific aspect, which turned the beholder to stone; especially—" Does "esp." mean especially?

HOLMES: An excellent guess. But, of course, to be really sure, you would have to look it up in the list of abbreviations at the back.

KEN: Well, I'm practically sure—"especially, Medusa." That tells me a little more. So just looking at them turned people to stone. They must have been nice girls to meet. [*cheerfully*] Well, now I know all about Medusa.

HOLMES: Do you, indeed? My dear young friend, do you for one moment suppose that I ever let a case drop half solved in that fashion?

WATSON: Why if you had, Holmes, the hound of the Baskervilles would still be the terror of the moors.

KEN: But, where should I look now?

HOLMES: Why, we haven't even touched the real reference books—the encyclopedias.

KEN: I did look in the encyclopedia. And there wasn't any—

HOLMES: Yes, yes. You said the same about the dictionary, I believe.

KEN: Yes. But, honestly, there isn't a thing in the encyclopedia.

HOLMES: Dear, dear. How the Britannica must be degenerating. You looked up Medusa?

KEN: Yes.

HOLMES: And it didn't tell you anything you wanted to know?

KEN: It only said—that is, it said to see something else— I suppose I should have looked that up then—It was just like the dictionary only I didn't understand what it meant.

HOLMES: Do you remember what heading it said to see?

KEN: No. Yes, I do too. It was "Gorgon." Just like the dictionary. I can look that up, can't I?

HOLMES: Yes, indeed. We'll solve this case yet, eh, Watson?

WATSON: I do think the boy shows great promise as a detective, Holmes.

KEN: Thank you, Doctor Watson. And here's a clue that even I know is here. I can tell which volume to use by looking at the letters on the back. Now, Gorgon will be in this volume because it's somewhere between GAME and GUNM. Right?

HOLMES: Right.

KEN: And I can find the page quickly by using these guide words at the top just as I did in the dictionary.

WATSON: Really amazing deduction, Kenneth.

KEN: Oh, I'm catching on to this detective stuff. [*Puts encyclopedia on table and finds place*] Yes, here it is. Quite a lot too. [*reading*] "Gorgon, gorgons. A figure, or figures, in Greek mythology. Homer says—" I'd better take some notes on this. [*Sits at table and takes out notebook and pencil*] This will be perfect.

21

HOLMES: [*peering through magnifying glass over Ken's shoulder*] You mean you're going to be satisfied with that little paragraph?

KEN: Where could I find more?

HOLMES: There's another encyclopedia set on the shelves.

KEN: Yes. There's Compton's. But won't both sets have the same stuff in them?

HOLMES: I should think it most unlikely. At any rate I wouldn't risk passing up an opportunity for information.

KEN: It's sort of "baby stuff" in Compton's, isn't it? We had that set way back in graded school.

HOLMES: It is rather simply written. However, some people—not you and I, of course—but, some people find the Britannica rather difficult to understand. I believe, that if the article in Compton's were read first the one in the Britannica might be a great deal easier to grasp. Of course, this is your case. If you feel you have it thoroughly solved—

KEN: No. I'll try Compton's. Here's the volume with G and H. [*taking it off shelves*] Gorgon—[*turning pages*] Let's see. Say, it just isn't here. Well, I'll try Medusa. [*Replaces volume and takes another from shelves*] Here's M. Now it ought to be—[*turning pages*] but it just isn't. That wasn't such a good idea, Sherlock Holmes, there's nothing about Gorgon *or* Medusa in here.

HOLMES: I hated to discourage you when you did so well on locating Gorgon in the other encyclopedia, but really you didn't go about that in the best possible way. You just had luck.

WATSON: No really scientific method about your work, my boy.

22

HOLMES: As Watson says. Of course, to be sure about locating what you want in an encyclopedia you use that best of all sources of clues—the index.

KEN: Does an encyclopedia have an index?

HOLMES: Certainly, my dear fellow. The Britannica has a separate index volume and Compton's has an index at the end of each volume. If this were my case I'd look up Medusa in the index of the M volume which you have there.

KEN: All right, but this Medusa is the most *elusive* thing. Harder to catch than an eel.

HOLMES: So are all criminals in really mysterious cases. That's what gives detective work its fascination.

KEN: I've found the index. Looks almost like the dictionary again, doesn't it? Now to locate the word. Medusa. Here she is! You needn't think you can escape me, my proud beauty. No sir, old detective Ken is on your trail. [*reading*] "Medusa, in Greek mythology, one of the Gorgons. P-127-8" [*blankly*] Now what does P-127-8 mean?

HOLMES: What would it mean? The letter, of course, refers to the—

KEN: The volume.

WATSON: Really, Holmes, the lad is improving.

HOLMES: And the numbers to—

KEN: The pages.

HOLMES: 'Pon my word, on my next big case, Ken, you shall be my assistant.

KEN: Thanks, Mr. Holmes, that will be great. Of course, you have some really interesting cases.

HOLMES: I never searched for anything more unusual than the Gorgon's head.

KEN: [*who has been busy locating the proper volume and page*] Got it! "The Greek hero who slew the Medusa." It's a regular story. I didn't know you could find anything like this in an encyclopedia. Will I have a report to make about the Medusa! [*Sits down at the table and begins to read with great attention, pausing to scribble occasional notes in his notebook. He is suddenly struck with a new idea*] You know, if I want still more information on this, I think I know where to find it.

HOLMES: Where, Ken?

KEN: I'll look up mythology in the catalog and I'll find where those books are on the shelves and I shouldn't wonder but what I'll find still more in the books.

WATSON: Bravo, Ken! He is doing excellently on this, isn't he now, Holmes? Give the lad the credit he's due.

HOLMES: Yes, Ken, that was a good piece of detective work.

KEN: I certainly appreciate your help, Mr. Holmes. And believe me, I'll remember all you told me about clues next time I want to look up anything.

WATSON: We solved this in wonderfully short order, Holmes.

HOLMES: Yes, *we* did, Watson. Just something to keep our hands in, eh what? But come, Watson, Ken doesn't need our help any further.

[*While Ken is absorbed in his reading and note taking Watson and Holmes step back behind the book stacks. After a moment's pause John comes in*]

JOHN: Hi, Ken! Did you find what you wanted to know?

KEN: I'll say. Look. Two long articles in the encyclopedia and a couple of definitions out of the dictionary. Just as soon as I get around to it I'm going to find some books on mythology and then I'll have still more. I'm going to have a recitation tomorrow that will just slay them.

JOHN: You're really good. How did you manage to dig up all that stuff?

KEN: My friend, Sherlock Holmes, here—

JOHN: Who? Where?

KEN: [*discovering for the first time that Holmes and Watson are no longer on the stage*] Sherlock Holmes! But they were here just a moment ago! Sherlock Holmes and Doctor Watson!

JOHN: [*Picks up the copy of the book* Adventures of Sherlock Holmes, *which Ken has left on the floor, and reads the title*] "Adventures of Sherlock Holmes." All I can say is, this is the first time I ever heard of anybody reading stories and having it help with a research topic. At any rate, I think you're a pretty smart guy to dig up all that information on an odd subject like that.

KEN: [*grandly*] Elementary, my dear John, elementary. Simply a matter of observation and deduction.

[CURTAIN]

25

The Juvenile Bookshop

by

VAUGHAN V. CUNNINGHAM

No royalty is requested unless an admission fee is charged to view the performance. In such cases a fee of $3 is to be paid to Miss Vaughan V. Cunningham, Apt. 6C, 333 East 41st Street, New York City.

This play was originally presented before the Mothers' Club of the Hamilton Fish Park Branch of the New York Public Library. The author suggests that it may be used as a vehicle to present old and new books for boys and girls by altering the part devoted to book discussion and by the telling of stories other than those selected.

TIME: Summer, 1765. Early afternoon.

SCENE: The story is set in the interior of Mr. John Newbery's bookshop in St. Paul's Churchyard, London. The stage shows two exits: one extreme *Lower Right*; the other extreme *Upper Left. Upper Right,* in the corner, is a small table on which are displayed a few of the haberdashery articles which Mr. Newbery has for sale. In *Upper Right Center* is a fireplace. On the right side of the mantel are a few bottles of Dr. James' Fever Powders attractively arranged; at the left end of the mantel is a small pile of brightly colored balls. Scattered here and there, mixed in with the balls and bottles are samples of Mr. Newbery's main stock in trade—books. *Upper Left Center*

UP STAGE

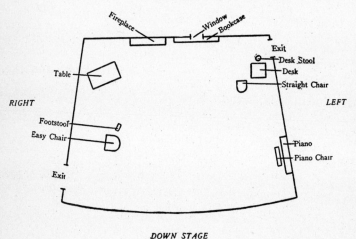

DOWN STAGE

29

is a bookcase, filled with small brightly covered books. Black and red pincushions are found on top of the bookcase at the right side. Just below the exit *Upper Left* is a small, tall desk with a stool behind it. Slightly *Down Right* from the desk is a straight chair. Extreme *Lower Left* is a piano which has been pushed into the wings so that it is only barely visible. Somewhat farther than half *Down Right* is a small easy chair which has been pushed out slightly toward the *Center*. A footstool is slightly *Up Left* from this chair. Prints may be hung above the fireplace and behind the desk; a small window above the bookcase admits light. Gay curtains at the window and cheerful covers for the chairs and footstool help give a light touch to the play.

CHARACTERS: MISTRESS ANNE PEFFNER, a young woman in her early twenties, is dressed in one of the more simple frocks of her day, of some light, sprigged material. She wears a hat that is rather ridiculous, albeit made without much effort of an oval board covered with material which matches the wide sash of her dress and much lace and flowers poised on top of the board. She ties it on with a ribbon, or is it a bit of veiling? Mistress Peffner strikes one as being a happy young lady and as being a person who does not mind speaking her mind.

MISTRESS CONSTANCE TILFNER, a friend of Mistress Peffner, is dressed in a frock and hat which, while they are not exact replicas, differ mostly in color and variety of flowers from those which her friend wears. Mistress Tilfner is somewhat more sober than Mistress Peffner, but she, also, is not a bit adverse to speaking her mind.

MISTRESS KATE, a girl of ten, is simply dressed in the costume of the time. She is not a "forward" child nor is she, on the other hand, a bashful one.

Her brother, eight year old MASTER JONATHAN, is somewhat more articulate than she, but is like her in that he is not distastefully aggressive but can take his part with ease and grace when included in adult conversation.

The NURSEMAID who escorts Mistress Kate and Master Jonathan and the CLERK found in Mr. Newbery's shop are quiet people who know how to efface themselves. We are but pleasantly aware of them at the opening of the play.

MUSIC AND OTHER SELECTIONS: The best version for telling "Bonnie Annot" can be found under the title "Habbitrot" in *The Fairy Cavern,* by Beatrix Potter (McKay. c1929); "The Barring of the Door" can be found in *Old Ballads in Prose,* by Eva March Tappan (Houghton. c1901); and "My Lady Greensleeves" is in The Esperance Morris Book, Pt. 1, by Mary Neal (J. Curwen & Sons, London. c1910)

30

The Juvenile Bookshop

[*Enter* MISTRESS ANNE PEFFNER *and* MISTRESS CONSTANCE TILFNER *from exit down right. Mistress Anne enters slightly in advance of Mistress Constance and speaks as she enters*]

MISTRESS ANNE: La, Mistress Constance, I do believe that there is nobody here. [*Mistress Anne crosses to left center while speaking; Mistress Constance crosses to right center*]

MISTRESS CONSTANCE: And that, Mistress Anne, surprises me not at all for I have heard it said that Master John Newbery is out of his shop so much people sometimes think he has forgotten he has one. Tell me, speaking of Master Newbery, what do you think of his great friend Dr. Samuel Johnson?

MISTRESS ANNE: A most extraordinary man! [*Sits down left on piano chair*] A strange person, they do say; and certainly most unattractive—even without making all the queer faces that he does. I don't believe I have ever seen him when he was wearing clean linen; nor does he wear his wig straight. [*Mistress Constance impatiently crosses up center*] I declare I would sooner see him without one. And then you must admit, Mistress Constance, that his gait is not an ordinary one!

MISTRESS CONSTANCE: La, Mistress Anne, I never thought you to be one who would repeat such unkind things! Unattractive Dr. Johnson may be and strange in his ways, but his talents are outstanding. There are few

31

who would deny that. Now Master Oliver Goldsmith—there's a different kettle of fish. [*Picks up a book from the bookcase*] I must own to a most unladylike curiosity in regard to Master Goldsmith and this little book, "The Renowned History of Little Goody Two-Shoes." [*Crossing down left slightly, hands the book to Mistress Anne who has crossed up right at the reference to "Little Goody Two-Shoes"*] He does squander his money so on beggars and friends and himself—though no one holds it against him—that it would not surprise me overly if he had attempted to fill his pocket with this little work.

MISTRESS ANNE: Oh, la, Mistress Constance, how you do go on. For myself, I think it most delightful that someone has had the kindness and the ability to give this little book, as Master Newbery says [*reading from book*], "To all young gentlemen and ladies who are good or intend to be good."

MISTRESS CONSTANCE: [*crossing down right as she speaks*] All very well, my good Mistress Anne, but there is one thing about that little book that is not delightful. I have this on rightful authority—that in the tale Master Newbery has caused to have inserted a reference to "Dr. James' Fever Powders," a compound that does one no good and even at times proves dangerous, which he sells. See, there is a bottle on that shelf [*Mistress Anne crosses up right center to look at bottle*] and that this story does so influence young ladies that at least one of them would have no medicine but this powder when she was ill. There! Mistress Anne, what do you say to that?

MISTRESS ANNE: I say, Mistress Constance, that that young lady must have had poor guidance by her elders! [*Crosses up left*] I'll grant you that Master Newbery knows little enough about medicine, but there is no one who can say me nay when I say he knows much about books. Look here at this "Little Pretty Pocket Book." According to the notice the price of a new book is six pence, for eight pence he will give a ball to every boy and a pincushion to every girl who buys one. Was it not of these you were speaking, Mistress Constance?

[*Offers a pincushion to Mistress Constance who accepts it*]

MISTRESS CONSTANCE: Yes, little sister Anne has one of these and there has been a marked improvement in her character since she acquired it. See—for every good deed one puts a pin in the red side and for every bad deed a pin goes in the black side [*suits action to word*]. It is quite remarkable to me that people can think of so many novel things.

[CLERK *enters from up left and, noticing that the ladies are engaged in conversation, does not interrupt them but busies himself at his desk*]

MISTRESS ANNE: And to me, Mistress Constance. Look you now at these "snuff box books" or "vest pocket books" as they are called. Not only are they pretty on the outside but their contents are most edifying—at the same time being entertaining. [*Picks up a book and continues talking as she crosses down stage right in front of Mistress Constance who crosses up left to the bookcase. Mistress Constance hesitates over the books a moment, selects two or three and then crosses down stage left where she sits. As she listens she casually pages the volumes she holds in her lap*] I am really quite taken by this "Little Pretty Pocket Book." Cousin Mabel had it lying on a table in her sitting room the other day and while I was passing the time until she had completed her arrangements for our drive I picked it up. Listen to this, Mistress Constance:

33

"Here's great K and L,
Pray Dame can you tell,
Who put the Pig-Hog
Down into the well?"

and [*turning pages rapidly*]

"So great O, and P,
Pray what do you see?
A naughty Boy whipt;
But that is not me."

These verses are decorated with pictures of children
playing such games as we played in our childhood. Do
you remember "Hoop and hide," "Boys and girls come
out to play," "I sent a letter to my love," "All the birds
in the air"? I do; and how we enjoyed them! In ad-
dition there are letters from "Jack the giant-killer" and
very pleasant and instructive they are, too. In my opin-
ion people have been in error in condemning "Jack the
giant-killer" as being too cruel for children. I don't
believe it affects them as much as mature persons sometimes assume. What have you there?

MISTRESS CONSTANCE: I am but glancing through "Little
Goody Two-Shoes" of which we spoke a short while
ago. At the beginning is written, "The History of Little
Goody Two-Shoes; Otherwise called, Mrs. Margery
Two-Shoes. With The Means by which she acquired
her Learning and Wisdom, and in consequence thereof
her Estate; set forth at large for the Benefit of those,

"Who, from a State of Rags and Care,
And having Shoes but half a Pair;
Their Fortune and their Fame would fix,
And gallop in a Coach and Six."

It seems to be a very fetching piece with good morals
drawn—having to do with two orphan children who are
thrust out into the world to provide for themselves.

34

The tale is most concerned with Mistress Margery Two-Shoes. I declare—even if it has been presented as a juvenile book—I should be most interested in reading it myself. Listen to this bit of verse:

> "In paper case,
> Hard by this place,
> Dead a poor dormouse lies;
> And soon or late,
> Summoned by Fate,
> Each Prince, each Monarch dies.
> Ye Sons of Verse,
> While I rehearse,
> Attend instructive rhyme;
> No sins had *Dor*
> To answer for—
> Repent of yours in time."

Is there not quite a moral in that, Mistress Anne?

MISTRESS ANNE: Indeed you are right, Mistress Constance. There is a marked lesson in that as there is also in this book called "Fables in Verse for the Improvement of Young and Old, by Abraham Aesop, Esq." [*Mistress Anne picks up a book from the mantel after having wandered up stage during Mistress Constance's speech about "Goody Two-Shoes"*] Oh, but here is "Mother Goose's Melody." [*She opens the book and walks down stage right, stopping just above the easy chair*]

Do you remember?

> "Lady Bird, Lady Bird
> Fly away home."

and

> "London Bridge is broken down,
> Dance o'er my Lady Lee;
> London Bridge is broken down,
> With a gay lady."

I wonder if this includes my old favorite of

> "Some little mice sat in a barn to spin;
>   Pussy came by, and popped her head in:
> 'What are you doing, my little men?'
> 'Weaving coats for gentlemen.'
> 'Shall I come in, and cut off your threads?'
> 'Oh, no! kind sir, you will snap off our heads.' "

[Mistress Anne examines the book, smiling and nodding her head in time with the rhythm of the verse she is silently reading. After a brief silence Mistress Constance speaks]

MISTRESS CONSTANCE: Here is "Giles Gingerbread." Do you remember hearing how he learned his lessons? His father gave him gingerbread on which had been stamped the alphabet and as Giles ate he learned. Now that is an idea that any who have dullards to deal with might profit by. *[Mistress Anne seats herself in the easy chair down stage right as Mistress Constance speaks]* I have been examining, too, this magazine. Will you listen to this: "The Lilliputian Magazine; or the Young Gentleman and Lady's Golden Library, being an Attempt to mend the World, to render the society of Man more Amiable, and to Establish the Plainness, Simplicity, Virtue and Wisdom of the Golden Age, so much celebrated by the Poets and Historians. . . ." It does seem to me that Master Newbery serves a vastly diversified fare to his patrons.

MISTRESS ANNE: That it does. In my childhood we were not so fortunate as to have available a juvenile library.

MISTRESS CONSTANCE: *[rising as she speaks and walking up stage right slightly, to pause with her back to the bookcase after disposing of the books she has been holding]* You speak truly, Mistress Anne; I well remember that most of the tales I knew were told to me. One of the ones I loved the best was "Bonnie Annot" and I am in a mood to repeat it to you if you would bear with me.

MISTRESS ANNE: Pray continue, Mistress Constance, it will please me.

[Enter MASTER JONATHAN *and* MISTRESS KATE *followed by a* NURSEMAID *from exit down right. Kate is carrying a violin case. As the children and their Nursemaid enter on Mistress Anne's last line they manage to get well on the stage before they are noticed]*

MISTRESS CONSTANCE: Why it's Mistress Kate and Master Jonathan.

[Mistress Anne rises and turns towards the newcomers]

MISTRESS ANNE *and* MISTRESS CONSTANCE: Good-day children. *[Kate curtsies, Jonathan bows; the Nursemaid makes her curtsy in response to a smile and nod from the ladies]*

MISTRESS KATE *and* MASTER JONATHAN: Good-day, Mistress Peffner. Good-day, Mistress Tilfner.

MISTRESS CONSTANCE: How is your dear mama? *[As she speaks she moves a little toward center stage; Mistress Anne moves toward the center]*

MISTRESS KATE: She is well, thank you.

MISTRESS ANNE: And your papa?

MASTER JONATHAN: He does well, thank you, Mistress Peffner.

MISTRESS CONSTANCE: And what brings you to Master Newbery's Juvenile Library? Have you come to purchase "A Little Pretty Pocket Book?" *[Nursemaid crosses to extreme left up stage, behind the groups; she and the Clerk talk together in inaudible tones]*

MISTRESS KATE: Not today, Mistress Tilfner; we are here upon Master Newbery's invitation to play for him and the great Dr. Johnson. *[She crosses left to the piano and puts her violin down]*

37

MASTER JONATHAN: And if Dr. Johnson thinks we do well and would amuse the gentlemen we are to play some time for his Club. [*Nursemaid and Clerk exit up left*]

MISTRESS CONSTANCE: That is an honor that you would do well to look forward to; but it seems that Master Newbery has forgotten his appointment. Come, play for us instead.

MISTRESS ANNE: [*crossing left, coming closer to the group*] Not so fast, Mistress Constance; have you forgotten that you were about to relate a tale to me? Come, commence once more—this time with a larger audience.

MISTRESS CONSTANCE: [*Curtsies to her friend*] Your persistence flatters me, Mistress Anne. Very well, I shall tell the tale, but upon one condition—nay, make it two: that Mistress Kate and Master Jonathan will play for us and that you shall yourself regale us with something from your memory.

MISTRESS ANNE: We are to have an afternoon of it?

MISTRESS CONSTANCE: Is it agreed?

ALL: It is agreed.

[*Mistress Anne crosses right and seats herself in the easy chair down right. Kate sits down stage left on the piano chair; Jonathan stands on the upstage side of Kate's chair. They all direct their attention to Mistress Constance who has crossed up stage center but seems unable to make up her mind where she should stand. She finally draws the straight chair below the Clerk's desk before the bookcase, seats herself in it and begins the old English folk tale "Bonnie Annot." After she has finished, her audience applauds*]

MISTRESS ANNE: It is a charming story and 'twas delightfully told.

MISTRESS KATE *and* MASTER JONATHAN: Thank you Mistress Tilfner.

MISTRESS CONSTANCE: Come now, Master Jonathan and Mistress Kate. According to the agreement you now have your cue.

[Kate gives her piano chair to Jonathan and crosses right to the footstool upstage from Mistress Anne's chair]

MASTER JONATHAN: If it would give the ladies pleasure I shall play "Lavender's Blue."

LAVENDER'S BLUE

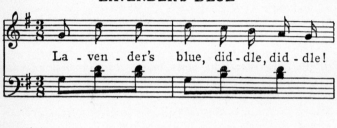

La - ven - der's blue, did - dle, did - dle!

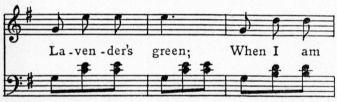

La - ven - der's green; When I am

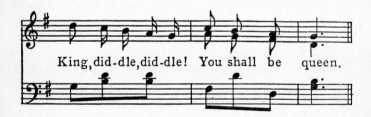

King, did-dle, did-dle! You shall be queen.

2. "Call up your men, diddle, diddle!
    Set them to work:
    Some to the plough, diddle, diddle!
    Some to the cart.

3. "Some to make hay, diddle, diddle!
    Some to cut corn:
    While you and I, diddle, diddle!
    Keep ourselves warm."

[*When he has brought the selection to a close everyone claps*]

MISTRESS CONSTANCE: Now Kate, 'tis your turn to play. Shall I accompany you and so let Jonathan rest?
[*Kate rises and curtsies, crosses left to the piano, politely waiting for Mistress Constance to precede her. Jonathan crosses right and seats himself on the footstool which Kate has just vacated. Kate removes her violin from its case and, after conferring with Mistress Constance, takes her position slightly up stage right from the piano. They play "My Lady Greensleeves." Their efforts are applauded. Mistress Anne rises while applauding and crosses to extreme left. She puts an arm around Kate*]

MISTRESS ANNE: That was delightfully rendered, my dears.

MISTRESS CONSTANCE: [*turning her chair to face center*] And now, Mistress Anne, a tale if you please.
[*Mistress Anne throws up her arms and crosses up stage toward the center. Kate crosses rapidly down right to seat herself in the chair beside Jonathan*]

MISTRESS ANNE: Since you insist! I shall tell a tale I often heard in my childhood. It was told to me in verse; but since the rhymes have left my head, I shall do my best in prose.
[*She pauses for a moment and then, with great spirit, tells "The Barring of the Door"—originally known in ballad form. As her story comes to a close, the curtain falls*]

40

Wings for Words
The Story of Johann Gutenberg
and His Invention of Printing

Written by

DOUGLAS C. McMURTRIE
With the collaboration of Don Farran

A Dramatization by

PETER J. KOESSLER

Wings for Words

SCENE: Johann Gutenberg's quarters in Strasbourg and his study in Mainz

TIME: Summer of 1438, 1439 and 1440, and Winter of 1468

CHARACTERS:

ANDRES DRITZEHEN ⎱
HANS RIFFE   ⎬ men in early 30's
MASTER HEILMANN ⎰

JOHANN GUTENBERG, at ages of 40 and 70

ENNELIN ZU DER ISERIN THURE, woman of 30

BISHOP OF STRASBOURG, man of 60

ULRICH GERING, young apprentice of 26

ACT I

SETTING: A room in Johann Gutenberg's quarters; at center, an oblong wooden bench; at the right, a high-backed chair; at the left, a small plain wooden stool.

TIME: Early evening on a day in August, 1438

ANDRES DRITZEHEN, seated at the center of the bench, is garbed in an orange robe of the period.

MASTER HEILMANN, seated at the left on the small stool, is dressed in light green.

HANS RIFFE stands at the left, his arms folded as if lost in deep thought. He is dressed in red.

[*As the curtain rises, an effect must be given as if a discussion had caused a momentary silence*]

ANDRES: Well, then, Hans Riffe—what dost say?

HANS: [*gruffly*] I say to thee, ask him the question thyself, Andres!

ANDRES: But thou knowest him so much better than myself.

43

HANS: If thou dost believe Johann Gutenberg possesses a secret of some invention in which ye can invest, find out for thyself. Ask him!

ANDRES: It be useless to talk to thee. Thou wast always a bullhead, Hans.

HANS: A bullhead am I called, because I do not wish to venture the anger of a friend with unseeming nosiness? Well enough dost thou know 'twas at my insistence we secured Johann's help and investment in the making of mirrors, for the pilgrimage to Aix-la-Chapelle. The beautiful pilgrimage which the kind mayor of the city has waylaid until the year 1440! So now sit we around with baskets full of mirrors in our laps and none will purchase them.

ANDRES: We all lost in that venture, thou as well as Johann and myself, Hans.

HANS: But Johann took time and toil to glean knowledge in the making of the mirrors.

ANDRES: True——

HANS: Then, too, with much patience did he explain the process of the work to us. His loss was much greater than our own, my friend.

HEILMANN: This friend of thine—this man Gutenberg—of whom I have heard so much, if all thou sayest is true, Hans, must be one who can adapt himself to many things.

HANS: Aye, that he can, Heilmann. Johann is filled with eagerness to possess himself of knowledge. He can cut woodblocks, is an expert at molding and sand casting, develops presses. His last work ere I betrayed him unwittingly into the mirror project was stone polishing and cutting.

ANDRES: He is much brilliant, yet Johann hath a secret. We must find out what it be.

HANS: And why?

ANDRES: Dost not need money, Hans?

HANS: [*Laughs*] As well as any other man.

ANDRES: Thou givest great trust to Johann Gutenberg?

HANS: More to him than to others!

ANDRES: Then if I worm this secret from him, wilt stand at our side and help in this work?

HANS: If it be agreeable to Johann to tell thee his secret, and he seeks our assistance, of a certainty will I stand at thy side.

ANDRES: Then will I question him myself!

HANS: [*Laughs*] Spoken like a man! [JOHANN GUTENBERG *enters from the right. He is dressed in black with red trimmings*] Oh, Johann, thou seest us resting in thy abode as if it were an inn.

JOHANN: [*happily*] Right glad am I to see ye all, friends. My home be thine as long as the roof caves not in. (*They all laugh*) How goes it with the mirror selling, Hans?

HANS: Must needs bring up that subject again, Johann? It is bitter irony for me to hear it so oft!

JOHANN: Irony? Mean it in that vein did I not. Forgive me.

ANDRES: Johann, this is a friend of mine, one Master Heilmann. He is much eager to make thy acquaintance.

JOHANN: [*Offers hand*] Welcome to our group, Master Heilmann! Shalt find our company robust and lacking in affection, yet true and deep in friendship.

HEILMANN: [*shaking hands*] Much honored am I, Johann Gutenberg, to make thy acquaintance.

JOHANN: Good, good! Well then, friends, what brings ye here today?

ANDRES: We seek to make money, Johann.

JOHANN: [*Laughs*] And so do I. What then shall we do to acquire it?

ANDRES: Positive am I, Johann, thou dost have a way if thou wert but mindful to tell of it.

JOHANN: What meanest thou there, Andres?

ANDRES: Johann, what is it thou hast worked on so long since the mirror venture? Couldst not teach us to help thee in the task as thou didst with the stone cutting? Surely with the four of us would the work—on whatever it may be—proceed faster.

JOHANN: [*Laughs*] Thou art blunt and straightforward, Andres—so also shall my answer be! Teach ye should I that which all my life I have been so zealously guarding? Once should others know my secret, so would the world have ears! Nay, nay, Andres! Ye know not what ye ask. Alone, must I give my work to the world— yet only when it be perfect!

ANDRES: And yet, Johann, thou hast worked on it a long time. Man can accomplish little or nothing alone. How oft do I see thee sitting and thinking, thinking of this great secret—for it must be great if thou dost give thy mind to it—and yet remains it undeveloped. In thy stubbornness and secretiveness mayest thou be withholding a benefit from mankind. Canst thou not trust us? Are we not thy friends?

[*Johann slowly walks up and down the room in deep thought. He suddenly turns and stops*]

JOHANN: Thy words have a grain of truth, Andres, more than thou knowest—[*pause*] Can it be thou art right in this? True, a man working alone can be much blind. With three to help me—perchance—perchance—would the dream come true!

ANDRES: All of us would do thy least bidding to assist——

JOHANN: Enough! I do it! My mind is filled with the thought—it dominates me and seeks companionship. We must find money for metals, paper and ink. If I make ye partners in this, do I give ye part of my life—

46

nay—almost all of it. Money and silence—that is my price, friends. Do ye agree?

HANS: We will keep thy secret.

ANDRES: And the money—somewhere shall we get it.

THOMAS: What is the price needed, Gutenberg?

JOHANN: One hundred and twenty-five gulden.

ANDRES: So much?

JOHANN: Fifty gulden as quickly as ye can. We must buy lead, paper, ink . . . and build a better press.

HANS: A press?

JOHANN: Aye! Even as a child in Mainz, and later as a young man ere the guilds banished me, did I cut and print woodblocks. As time passed did I use hundreds of individual metal letters which could be assembled into sentences—letter by letter, until there would be whole pages, closely resembling those written with great care by scribes.

ANDRES: But the press, Johann—a wine press?

JOHANN: [enthused] A press, yes! But no longer merely a wine press. Much improvement does mine need. We must build into it a proper bed for the page of metal letters, on which it can rest, and a frame to hold the paper away from the letters until the moment we can pull the screw around to bring them together. The press will work much better and smoother than drawing impressions by rubbing paper against woodblocks!

HANS: All this leaves me in perplexity!

JOHANN: So far have I gone; much remains to solve. Much have I to teach. Much must ye learn. Yet if we can find the complete secret, then can we print books for mankind and give wings to words!

ANDRES: Books—so that's it! All this hast thou thought out—and all alone!

JOHANN: [softly] Nay, not completely alone. A friend of my childhood, one Relf Ahrens, long since gone to

Holland, shared my secret longing. His poor father, grinded by taxes, could ill afford to send the boy to school. So did I, in mine eagerness to teach him reading, wearily copy for him my Latin grammar Donatus in longhand· Thus was born in me the idea to make quicker and better books—books cheaper for the poor to buy, and give knowledge to their young.

HEILMANN: A noble thought, friend.

ANDRES: But this press—who will build it for us, Johann?

JOHANN: Go ye at once to Conrad Saspach. Do not delay. He is a secretive man if he be paid for his toil. Ask his agreement to build our press.

HANS: I know him well, Johann. Fear not, he shall be able to guard his tongue and build as thou dost instruct.

ANDRES: Good! Then we go. Later, Johann, shall we return to impart the news to thee.

JOHANN: Do so—and remember——[*He puts his finger to his lips*] The silence of the grave!

HEILMAN: Aye!

HANS: Farewell, Johann.

JOHANN: Farewell, all.

[*The three men exeunt at the right. Johann looks after them a moment.* ENNELIN ZU DER ISERIN THURE *enters at the left. She comes forward· Her gown is violet*]

ENNELIN: [*softly*] Johann!

JOHANN: [*Turns*] Ennelin! This is a pleasant surprise.

ENNELIN: Hidden have I been in thy study until thy friends made their departure—a long time have I waited for thee.

JOHANN: True, true, Ennelin! What a wretch am I——

ENNELIN: [*coyly*] Thou didst promise to take me to the fair this evening. Yet hast thou forgotten, Johann.

JOHANN: Nay, nay! I had not forgotten. Enmeshed was I in much thinking of future work——

ENNELIN: Future work?

48

JOHANN: Our future work, Ennelin—the work which shall make our married life one of joyous respect and plenty.

ENNELIN: [*laughing gently*] Is it thus thou dost ask me to become thy wife, Johann Gutenberg?

JOHANN: [*Takes her hand*] Not well am I versed in the affairs of courting. Yet this much know I—no other woman shall I seek if thou dost refuse to become my wife.

ENNELIN: Rest ye there, Johann. Men are fickle, even as women, in love. Yet do I well believe thy words. Thou art honest and blunt and filled with deep sincerity.

JOHANN: Shall we then to the fair, to celebrate this joyous evening? Shall we shout to the world that our love will be strong and enduring?

ENNELIN: [*Laughs*] Thou art even as a schoolboy!

JOHANN: As even a schoolboy! One who has gleaned knowledge of a great secret——[*pause*] Aye—a great secret——

ENNELIN: What is it, Johann? Thy face doth wear a sombre look.

JOHANN: Nay, nay. Enough. 'Twas but a momentary thought. Come to the fair where the dancers await us! [*He seizes her hand, leads her to the right as the curtain falls*]

ACT II

TIME: The twilight of a day in July, 1439
SETTING: Gutenberg's workroom; in the center of the room, a small press; at the right of it, a table filled with materials; at the left, an oblong bench.
The stage is deserted at rise of curtain.

[ENNELIN *enters from the left. She looks around the room somewhat disdainfully, crosses to the right, and as she passes the press lifts her skirts as if in scorn*]

ENNELIN: [*Calls*] Johann! Johann! [*There is no answer. Ennelin shrugs her shoulders and slowly walks to the table. She looks at the material and shakes her head. She then crosses to the press and lifts up a dirty, ink-stained rag, and gives an exclamation of disgust, dropping it quickly. Again she crosses to the right and calls louder*] Johann! Johann, come down—'tis Ennelin! [*She slowly walks to the bench at left and sits down as if in deep thought. JOHANN enters from the right. He looks somewhat grimy and dirty and seems much fatigued*]

JOHANN: Sorry am I, Ennelin, to have made thee wait for me. Yet did fatigue and weariness so assail my mind and body, that a slight rest was of great necessity.

ENNELIN: Working thyself to death for naught? Still experimenting with the printing?

JOHANN: With the printing, yes.

ENNELIN: Thou dost have the appearance of a common laborer, Johann. Thy hands are much ink-stained.

JOHANN: [*Laughs*] Ah, my hands! [*Looks at them*] If that were all, Ennelin! The ink hath stained my heart and mind, too.

50

ENNELIN: Come to thy shop, did I, to ask thee a question, Johann.

JOHANN: Aye? What is it, Ennelin?

ENNELIN: Why didst thou so humiliate me in this lawsuit against George Dritzehen?

JOHANN: Humiliate thee? It was not my intention to do such a deed. I merely fought for what was rightfully mine. Andres Dritzehen had a contract with me in the printing. Yet at his death did his brother, George forcefully wish to become my partner. The courts decreed otherwise. We were in the right and received the favor of the law.

ENNELIN: George Dritzehen is my friend. He was the cause of our acquaintance. Hast forgotten that?

JOHANN: Nay——

ENNELIN: Then, too, all the townspeople of Strasbourg do gossip about thee behind thy back because of this lawsuit. And then—experimenting—experimenting forever. Some call thee mad behind thy back——

JOHANN: [*Laughs*] That is their privilege, Ennelin. Let us not quarrel because of gossip——

ENNELIN: But I am a woman, Johann, and want a home —a home for us. We grow not younger.

JOHANN: I understand, Ennelin. Have I not promised thee marriage? Thou dost love me surely?

ENNELIN: Yes. But—but—this foolishness—this printing —it goes on forever. Will it go on even after our marriage? Wilt thou spend all thou hast on these fruitless experimentations?

JOHANN: I must go on, Ennelin, if ever I am to find a way. What would I do if I did give up the venture now? What am I supposed to do? After all these years of struggle, am I to throw over all this labor for——

51

ENNELIN: For me? Yes!!—[*pause*] If thou didst love me, would ye do it!

JOHANN: [*softly*] That——can I not.

ENNELIN: Then 'tis true? All my friends and relations did tell me thou wast a fanatic, a madman who lives in a dream!

JOHANN: A dream? Yes, if thou dost call it that. A dream. Canst not understand? If I can find a way to make books, I can give words wings to fly from land to land, helping men to share everything they know. Some words will be bitter and strong, yet true. Others will be beautiful, full of knowledge and understanding, enabling man to live better in peace and justice——

ENNELIN: [*Rises*] Not only a dream is this, but a nightmare.

JOHANN: A nightmare?

ENNELIN: Yes, a nightmare, hidden in the brain of a willful, stubborn man who will not live as other men do——

JOHANN: I cannot give up my life's work! I must not give it up! Even if by holding to it do I lose thee——

ENNELIN: Johann!

JOHANN: Forgive me! My heart had hoped thou wouldst understand——

ENNELIN: Nay, I am only a woman! To me there is little value in paper and sticky black ink! Glad am I thou hast spoken so to me. Readily do I realize all thy time, thought and money would be wasted on this invention. [*She starts to go*]

JOHANN: Nay, Ennelin—hear me out——

ENNELIN: Enough have I heard, Johann. We part here. All our future dreams of a happy marriage hast thou ruthlessly shattered. This only I know—Wasted my time have I with a man who loves me not. Farewell! [*Ennelin exits at the right*]

JOHANN: [*Calls*] Ennelin!

52

[*He listens a moment, then shakes his head and walks to the press and leans upon it heavily. He then quickly covers his face with his hand and rests on the bench at left. A moment of silence. Then the* BISHOP OF STRASBOURG *enters from the right. He looks at Johann smilingly and gently comes forward, resting his hand on Johann's shoulder*]

BISHOP: Ah, Johann—deep in thought of the future?

JOHANN: [*Rises*] Your grace! Pardon me, I had not heard thy approach——

BISHOP: Sit ye down, my son. Rest—thou dost look weary and fatigued.

JOHANN: [*Sits*] True, true. I am weary and heartsick, my thought is full——

BISHOP: [*Sits beside him*] Thought is a rare treasure, my friend. Yet too much thinking of one particular thing can undermine health and strength. Well has thou labored in thy experiments of printing—but thou must rest.

JOHANN: Rest? Rest comes to me not. The thought of books for mankind drives me on. Know ye what befell me today—because of them, your grace?

BISHOP: Nay, friend, what hast befallen thee?

JOHANN: Well knowest thou worldly thoughts of life and pleasure ne'er dominated my brain. Yet today, because of this very love I bear my work, did I lose the only woman my heart did e'er desire.

BISHOP: Ennelin?

JOHANN: Aye, Ennelin! With heartiness did she upbraid me, and now hath left me.

BISHOP: She seeks what all women seek—security, a home for her husband and children. Bear not bitterness against her because of that fact. Life goes on, as a never-ending river. Men of thy calibre, in the hope of future inventions, if wedded to the marriage law, usually bring

53

unhappiness to the loved ones. Thou must go forward, to complete the work thou hast begun. Bring light to mankind as it stumbleth in the darkness.

JOHANN: Thy words do bring helpful consolation. Some day in the future will my weary brain conceive a way to complete my experimentations. Then shall I print my Donatus for all the world to see!

BISHOP: [*Smiles*] Ah, thy Donatus—the little Latin grammar thou didst copy wearily by hand to give to thy young friend, Relf Ahrens?

JOHANN: Aye, long, long ago was it——

BISHOP: Thou must rest and come to our scriptorium. There wilt thou see with what patience the brown-robed monks do copy books by hand to benefit mankind. There canst thou read and study great books, improve thy mind and rest. Bring thy working companions with thee. Rest ye a month or more with us, and return again to this task of printing, which hath been thy life's work. So shalt thou return refreshed and cheered in thy future endeavours.

JOHANN: Much thanks do I give thee, your grace. Thy advice and hospitality come from the kindness of thy heart.

BISHOP: It comes from my thought, Johann, which sees in thee the hope of a better world.

[*They look at each other as the curtain falls*]

ACT III

Time: Summer, 1440, near midnight
Setting: Gutenberg's workshop

[*As the curtain rises* Hans Riffe *is working at the press, center.* Master Heilmann *is bent over the table, right, busily working. The* Bishop *sits on the bench. An effect must be given as if a conversation had been in progress*]

Bishop: ——so this then the reason for Johann's absence from my side?

Hans: [*excitedly*] Aye—your grace! Much labor and thought did it require. Yet now we are at the threshold of a great secret!

Bishop: God moves in mysterious ways! The discovery of the L-shaped forms, which can make this perfect mold to guide the letters, happened to Johann as he was eating his mid-day meal, ye say?

Hans: [*Laughs*] Aye, that it did! On a piece of rye bread was he chewing when he made this great discovery.

Heilmann: The L-shaped metal pieces make a perfect mold. Each type is now accurate in size and shape, and all letters of one kind are exactly the same, no matter how many of them we make.

Hans: All prepared are we to make the great experiment. When Johann returns, shall we begin to set up a complete page.

Bishop: What page and from what book have ye set up for this new attempt?

55

HANS: [*Smiles*] Need'st thou ask, your grace? It is even the beginning of that self-same book for which Johann hath such great love.

BISHOP: Thou meanest the Latin grammar, Donatus?

HANS: The same is it.

[JOHANN *enters hastily from the right. The Bishop rises*]

BISHOP: Ah, Johann! Since thou dost neglect to visit me, have I come to thy dwelling——

JOHANN: [*crossing to him eagerly*] Your grace! Thank God thou art here! Thou, of all those I know, art one who hath helped and offered consolation in my darkest hours. At last—at last—do I attempt to bring printing to the world!

BISHOP: Thy helpmates here have told me of thy great discovery, Johann. Said I not always thou wouldst some day, with hard labor and great pain, accomplish the deed?

JOHANN: Aye, true, that thou hast. [*He turns to the men*] Now then, Hans——Heilmann——Shall we attempt the deed? Are ye ready?

HANS: No, not yet, Johann. Only a few lines of the first page of the Donatus are set.

JOHANN: Come, enough! Let us use what lines ye have. I cannot wait any longer! So will we soon discover if all our many nights and days of weary and laborious toil shall produce a fruit.

[*They turn to the press, Hans and Heilmann with the materials. The test is arranged*]

JOHANN: It is ready! Now, then—turn the screw, Hans! [*Hans turns the screw. They watch breathlessly*] Now —reverse it.

[*Hans does so. The plate retreats upward. Johann carefully lifts the paper from the types as the frame releases them. Johann passes a hand rapidly across his face and looks at the paper. The others look at him in expectancy.*]

56

Silently Johann hands the paper to the Bishop, who takes it]

BISHOP: [*softly as he looks at the paper*] Blessed be God! [*The Bishop hands the paper to Hans. Hans looks at it with Heilmann peering over his shoulder*]

JOHANN: [*softly*] It hath been done! A dream come from childhood! We print! We print! For all the world to see!

HANS: [*Throws arm around Johann*] My friend, what a day of joy is this for thee!

JOHANN: [*Laughs*] For me? Not only for me but for all the world!

BISHOP: Thou art right, my son. It hath taken thee years to discover this deed. Much labor, courage and determination did it require. Yet what the years, in their fast moving flight, have taken from thee, will mankind bring to thee in its reward of remembrance in future ages.

JOHANN: To print—books! Books!! Scarce can I believe it!

BISHOP: One book must ye set up, my son, even the great book which all the world knows—the Bible. So then will all humanity be able to read easily the words of the ages.

JOHANN: True, your grace. So shall it be one day. Yet now must needs I hold a promise given as a child to myself and one other. First must I print the Latin grammar—Donatus!

BISHOP: [*Smiles*] I see. Little did I realize that the Donatus meant so much to thee.

JOHANN: It doth, your grace. Later the Bible, now the Donatus! The problems of this work are many. Half of them have we not solved. The Bible hath so many pages, words and letters—years would it take——

BISHOP: [*happily*] Enough, my son! Print thou thy beloved Donatus.

JOHANN: Come, friends, we go to work with a will, knowing we are in the right. All the world shall now see the power and benefit of the printed word. Words no longer hard to find, but words on wings, carrying knowledge over the face of the earth! Full well, long may we remember this year—1440! Come, we begin——

[*The curtain quickly falls*]

ACT IV

TIME: Late February in 1468. Twilight.

SETTING: The study in Gutenberg's home in Mainz; the room is flooded with a violet and amber glow. GUTENBERG is seated at the center in a high-backed chair. At his left, a small table, on which a book rests. At his right, on a plain wooden stool, sits one of his pupils—ULRICH GERING. Gutenberg is aged—his hair is completely gray. Ulrich is a young fellow of 26. Gutenberg is dressed in red and black, Ulrich in dark green.

[*As the curtain rises Johann is speaking. An effect must be given as if he had been talking for a long while*]

JOHANN: ——and so it was, my lad. That was the joyous year—1440. Indeed, indeed—a long time ago. A very long time ago. Young was I then—grim, eager, determined in my hope of the success in printing. And now am I seventy. Yet nothing in life, in all those years vanished, hath given me more rapture, than that moment when with trembling hand I clutched the first page of the Donatus to my heart.

ULRICH: Yes, yes, the Donatus! Thou must tell me more of it, Master Gutenberg——

JOHANN: [*Smiles*] Art much filled with eagerness to have knowledge of our trade, Ulrich Gering. These years gone by hast been an excellent student and an apt pupil at my side. Hark then. With deep joy and excitement did we begin to print the Donatus. Letter by letter, word by word, page by page. One hundred copies of each page, until all twenty-eight of the book had been finished, and seven piles of sheets were stacked on the table. Months had it taken us, much labor and many disappointments did we encounter. Soft lead types

59

slowly wore down, new types were cast. Oft did the ink dry out; new ink was supplied. And yet, when finished at last, only one-tenth of the time had the one hundred copies required, than ordinarily taken by a scribe to make as many books.

ULRICH: And then—and then, what happened, Master Gutenberg? What astonishment did the townspeople give?

JOHANN: [*Laughs*] Well mayest thou ask, Ulrich! The good Bishop of Strasbourg praised God at the sight of the Donatus. On the other hand, the mayor, shocked at the creation, pronounced it had been produced by the devil and black magic! Citizens thronged our shop to see the invented press, and looked upon it as a miracle. Scribes were furious and wished to do us violence. But the bishop, in the kindness of his heart, and because he, too, gazed into the future, issued a statement defending our invention. Thus were we not molested by the ignorant.

ULRICH: And who, Master Gutenberg, secured the copies of the valued book? The children—the boys for whom thou hadst so eagerly worked all those years?

JOHANN: Alas, nay. They later secured them. At first, the wealthy vied to buy the book at exorbitant prices, and so did it prove to us with what determination all people wanted our books. One—two—nay, for three years long did we print the Donatus until fifteen editions had been born. Travelers, traders and merchants passing through the city eagerly purchased and carried the books to all corners of Europe. [*He picks up the book on the table*] The "magic" in this little book was changing the thought of humanity, and would change the face in Europe in time to come.

[*Ulrich eagerly puts out his hand. Johann hands it to him*]

ULRICH: [*Pauses, looking at the book*] The first Donatus! And then, Master Gutenberg—the Bible—the great work—?

JOHANN: Ah, yes—the Bible! What agony did it cost my soul! Yet all great works are born amid great pain and havoc. My beloved Bible was not an exception. One Master Fust had been my partner in the attempted production of my first Bible. A business man he was, kind but firm and eager for profit——. My dreams to make the Bible more beautiful in printing, my determination to perfect the trade, made me lose thought of time. So at last these things brought his anger upon my head, and with the force of the law on his side, because of his vast loans to me, did they strip me of all my working possessions.

ULRICH: [*angrily*] Heartless was he, an ignorant man——

JOHANN: Nay, lad, he was but a cautious one. Money dominated him. Returns did he seek from his investments. Other did he then employ to take my place to complete the Bible. And so at last, in the year 1456, did he succeed in bringing the Holy Book before the eyes of the world. My name appeared *nowhere* in the book of books. Deep was the wound that arrow caused. Vast was the pain in my heart——[*pause*]

ULRICH: [*eagerly*] But thou didst go on?

JOHANN: Aye, lad, that I did. With more fury than ever, did I believe in my dream of the Bible—a Bible better than the one printed by Master Fust and his associates. So with the help of many kind souls, who gave me aid, mentally and financially, did I, at last, complete my own Bible in 1459——[*pause*] Yet enough of this. Not to enumerate to thee my tribulations and joys, young Ulrich, did I summon thee to me! Work have I for thee to do.

61

ULRICH: Anything, Master Gutenberg—but give the command, thou shalt not find me wanting in obedience.

JOHANN: Oft have I heard thee express a longing to visit and work at the University of Paris.

ULRICH: Aye, 'tis true.

JOHANN: Of late hath the University of Paris kindly entreated me to send them printers, to help them in their great work of dispersing knowledge to the young. Wilt go, Ulrich?

ULRICH: [*Rises*] I, Master? To Paris? To the University?

JOHANN: Even so. Thou, Ulrich Gering. At thy side shall I send two other of my printers, Michael Friburger and Martin Crantz. Ye must work together, and build a press for the University.

ULRICH: [*overjoyed*] Master Gutenberg, thy kindness overwhelms me——I——

JOHANN: Nay, nay, lad, go not too fast. Much labor will it require. But I have faith in thee. Teach others to print, so they, too, can give wings to words.

ULRICH: Do we go at once, Master?

JOHANN: [*Rises*] Tomorrow, lad. Thou shalt go tomorrow. Tell Paris I eagerly share my knowledge with it through thee. Were I younger, would I go with thee. Go, now— say nothing! Farewells are not easy for me in my years. God bless thee.

[*They look at each other a moment. Ulrich then bows and quickly exits. Johann stands a moment in thought, then walks to the table and gently picks up the Donatus. He slowly sits down fondling the book*]

JOHANN: Thou little child of long ago—Donatus of old. Here we ponder, as I hold thee in my hand, growing old together. Heavy, weary and arduous was thy birth. Full many of thy kind now fill the world. In centuries to come wilt thou be surrounded by many, many sisters

—glowing and majestic in beauty, wisdom and humanity. Yet all—*all*—gleaned knowledge in the study of thy printed face, that face, which is the reflection of my life's toil and devotion to mankind's progress.

[*The curtain slowly falls as Johann looks into the future*]

The Guilty Ones
By
Ruth Amelia Smith

Given at the Jefferson Junior High School, Meriden, Conn., this play was so well liked by the students that they signed a petition to repeat it in the evening for the parents.

TIME: The present.

Action takes place in about one hour—not more.

Properties and business can be as elaborate as desired. If the girls and boys are capable they may "ad lib" to a certain extent. Business to suit may be worked in for jury, reporters, stenographer, and attorneys, but not so as to detract from main procedure.

CHARACTERS:

JUDGE—short boy
DISTRICT ATTORNEY—tall boy
ATTORNEY FOR THE DEFENSE—
    of medium height
CLERK OF THE COURT—boy of
    medium height
COURT STENOGRAPHER—boy or girl
12 JURORS—6 girls and 6 boys
4 REPORTERS—2 boys and 2 girls
2 OFFICERS—2 boys
MR. MAGAZINES
MR. BOYS' LIFE

MISS CHEWING GUM
MRS. LIBRARIAN JONES
MR. COMMON NUISANCE
MR. WANDERING BOY
MISS FIGGETTS GOSSIP
MISS RATTLE TRAP
MR. OVERDUE BOOKS
MISS DUE DATE
MR. NON-FICTION
MR. BIOGRAPHY
MISS SHELVERS
MR. BOOK TRUCK

SCENE: A court room.

The Judge's desk and stool are raised above the others; a stuffed owl graces his desk. Gavel on desk. Horn for sound of cow moo back stage. There are a table and four chairs for reporters; paper, pencils, notebooks, bottles of ink, etc., on table. Table for the clerk of the court on which is a large dictionary. Chair for clerk.

Two desks or small tables, one on either side of stage, for District Attorney and Attorney for the Defense. Several large books on tables, two chairs. Twelve chairs for jury—may be roped off to denote jury box.

One chair on podium for prisoner's use.

Typewriter table, typewriter, and chair for stenographer. A score board may be used if desirable.

Witnesses may remain standing. Two officers stand.

SUGGESTIONS FOR COSTUMING: Judge: Cap and gown, black beard and mustache, horn-rimmed glasses without lenses, large white hand-

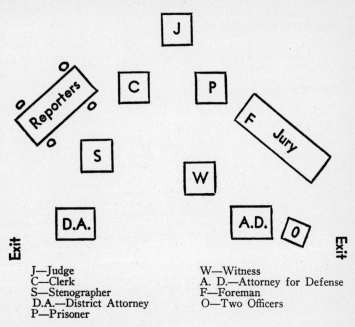

J—Judge
C—Clerk
S—Stenographer
D.A.—District Attorney
P—Prisoner

W—Witness
A. D.—Attorney for Defense
F—Foreman
O—Two Officers

kerchief, golf sticks and bag and moo cow which can be procured at Five and Ten, at Hallowe'en. Gavel.

ATTORNEYS: One in long-tailed coat, one in short, tight-fitting coat; black and white striped or checked trousers, large red or blue handkerchiefs, may wear flowers in lapels, several pencils in breast pockets. One may have large red apple, one a sandwich. Notebooks, papers, several large books, brief cases; mustaches differ—one small and close, one long and flowing.

CLERK OF COURT: Uses large dictionary to swear in prisoners and witnesses. In ordinary suit.

TWELVE JURORS AND FOUR REPORTERS: Dress to suit own ideas.

COURT STENOGRAPHER: Extra long pencil behind ear, if boy. Has nothing to say but may strike typewriter keys occasionally and inject a certain amount of humorous business from time to time. Dress as seems advisable.

TWO OFFICERS: Dark blue suits, police hats, belts. Carry clubs and handcuffs, which may be used if desired. Large badges saying "Police" can be made from cardboard, covered with silver paper.

PRISONERS AND WITNESSES may dress to suit the parts as nearly as possible or may use everyday clothes. For instance, Mr. Magazines could have torn leaves from magazines pinned to his suit. If they can fit themselves to their parts, however, that may be sufficient; for instance, Miss Gossip and Miss Chewing Gum have excellent opportunities. Mr. Book Truck might be on roller skates.

A box for names may be concealed on clerk's table. Twelve slips of paper with names of jury written on them should be ready for use.

Jury should be sitting in different sections of auditorium and proceed to stage and jury box as called. Foreman will sit on end, first row nearest Judge. Less confusion is caused if back row is filled in first.

ACTION ON OPENING. Scene may be laid either in front of curtains, if large stage, or entire stage may be used if small stage. Characters may enter from off stage or through aisles of auditorium.

DISTRICT ATTORNEY and ATTORNEY FOR THE DEFENSE enter carrying arms full of books and brief cases, arguing. Take seats, pull out quantities of sheets of paper and proceed to arrange; one puts large red apple on desk, one has wrapped sandwich sticking out of pocket. FOUR REPORTERS enter talking and laughing. Arrange notebooks and pencils. COURT STENOGRAPHER follows—sits—tries typewriter. Powders face if girl. TWO OFFICERS appear. After a minute all look expectantly for Judge.

Then JUDGE proceeds through center aisle holding up gown with each hand, golf clubs in bag under arm. This should be rather a struggle as Judge is a small boy. CLERK follows Judge, holding up his gown in back.

Prisoners and witnesses are off stage left.

All rise as Judge enters. Then all are quiet and give attention to Judge who raps loudly with gavel. Then remembers golf clubs. Judge places golf sticks. If they fall and scatter and have to be rescued and picked up so much the better.

69

The Guilty Ones

A COMEDY OF MISDEMEANORS IN ONE ACT

JUDGE: [*Raps again*] Order in the court! Ladies and Gentlemen—[*impressively and slowly*] be seated! [*loudly, looking over glasses at empty chairs of jury*] Well, well, [*testily*] where's the jury? Late again? How can I have a trial without a jury?

CLERK: [*rising*] No, your Honor. They're on a stand-up strike at home. They want more time for football. [*Suit game to season*]

JUDGE: Oh, they are, are they? They do, do they? Well, do something! Get a jury! I can't stay around here all day. [*Looks affectionately at golf clubs*]

CLERK: All right, don't get upset. I suggest we draw a jury from the audience.

REPORTERS: Oh! Fun.

JUDGE: [*Raps*] Order in the court! [*Snaps*] Get to it. I can't spend all my time in court. [*Examines one of his golf clubs*]
[*Clerk pulls slips out of box one by one and calls names until twelve have been called. The twelve proceed to chairs in jurors' box on stage*]

JUDGE: [*Raps loudly*] Order in the court! [*Someone giggles—he raps again*] If ye giggle, ye're out and I don't mean maybe!
[*All are quiet, look at Judge*]

JUDGE: Clerk, read the case.

CLERK: The first case on the docket is "The Library versus Mr. Magazines" charged with disorderly conduct in the worst degree.

71

JUDGE: Officers, bring in the prisoner. [*Officers go off left*]

DISTRICT ATTORNEY: [*swaggering*] I intend to prove that Mr. Magazines is a torn, worn, disreputable individual who not only is disorderly but has loose pages and a dirty face. He is a disgrace to the rack on which he lives in the library.

ATTORNEY FOR DEFENSE: Know it all, don't you?

[*Officers return with* MR. MAGAZINES *between them. He is handcuffed, and hangs his head in shame. Acts very confused*]

D. A.: Officers, produce the witness.

OFFICERS: Aye, aye sir! [*Salute*]

[*Officers go off left, return with* MR. BOYS' LIFE]

CLERK: [*Steps forward holding dictionary out to Mr. Boys' Life. Says so rapidly as to be unintelligible*] Do you swear to tell the truth, the whole truth and nothing but the truth, so help you anyone who can?

MR. BOYS' LIFE: I do, if it doesn't cost anything.

[*Clerk sits*]

D. A.: Now, my good man, what's your name?

MR. B. L.: Boys' Life and I try to be good men according to the Boy Scout Law.

D. A.: Where do you live?

MR. B. L.: On the magazine rack in the . . . . library.

D. A.: What's your age?

MR. B. L.: Well, I'll be frank with you—I haven't any.

D. A.: Nonsense! Everybody has an age—"Living Age"; "Mechanical Age"; Age before Beauty; Seven Ages of Man.

A. D.: I object, your Honor, this is irrelevant, immaterial and of no use!

JUDGE: Objection sustained. Proceed, Mr. D. A., and no more wise cracks.

D. A.: Well, why haven't you an age?

MR. B. L.: Oh! I'm just a new copy every month and if
you ask me I need to be. [*looking belligerent*]

D. A.: Nobody asked you, go on.

MR. B. L.: That's what I do. Proceed from September to
September and then start all over again. I'm like Peter
Pan, I never grow up.

D. A.: You mean you're actually twelve years old, why
didn't you say so?

MR. B. L.: Exactly, my fine fellow—Charlie McCarthy and
I are twelve years old. Say, he's great, isn't he?

D. A.: Please keep to the subject, object, verb, ho-hum but
I'm tired. [*Stifles yawn*]

JUDGE: [*chiming in*] Who's tired? *I'm* tired. Bowling,
tennis, golf—ah! golf! [*Looks at golf clubs, wistfully*]

A. D.: [*jumping up*] That's it! That's it! [*excitedly*]
That's the word. I've been trying to think of that word.
[*Turns to judge*] Your Honor, I object.

JUDGE: [*nodding, snores loudly—straightens glasses, raps
loudly*] Huh! What say? Oh! Yes—I know you—I've
seen you at the Tigers' Club, or was it the Golf Club?
[*Laughs*] Ha! Ha! Ha!

A. D.: [*shouting*] Now you listen to me, Judge, I say I
object and I mean I object!

JUDGE: What for? I thought things were going all right—
a bit slow, but I'll get pepped up at the Golf Club. Why
disturb me?

A. D.: [*sadly*] Oh—dear!

D. A.: Culprit, tell your story. What do you know about
Mr. Magazines?

[*Mr. Magazines hangs head, shuffles feet, looks uneasy*]

MR. B. L.: In September when I came to this school I
thought I had got into a grand place. I was duly
checked in and stamped and proudly took my place on
the magazine rack. I was comfortable and expected to
be admired. Goodness knows I'm a fine looker. But in

a few days my spirits were dampened. The pupils began pushing me around, putting me anywhere but where I belonged. They put me backwards, upside down and got me generally confused. It's an outrage! From my own experience I know this happened to Mr. Magazines and he was not disorderly of his own free will.

D. A.: Ha! Ha! Huh! Huh! I see. Birds of a feather. I think you ought to be arrested, too.

A. D.: I object.

JUDGE: Seems as though we have more objects than subjects. That can't be right. Ask any English teacher.

D. A.: I ask you, Mr. Boys' Life, has he a dirty face or hasn't he?

MR. B. L.: Yes, 'tis true, but please, kind sir, it's not his fault.

D. A.: Say, your Honor, I'm not your kind sir.

MR. B. L.: Yes—your Honor—so I noticed.

D. A.: Enough! I have shown clearly that Mr. Magazines was disorderly and has a dirty face.

A. D.: Now, listen to me, I've shown more clearly that Mr. Magazines was not wilfully disorderly and the pupils made his face dirty and tore his clothes and pushed him around. Jury, it's up to you. Do this man a favor—let him go back to his rightful place on the magazine rack with his good friend, Boys' Life, and let them stay there in peace.

JUDGE: Time for a verdict. I can't sleep here all day. Jury, do your duty. Man's not guilty, of course, but don't let me prejudice you.

[*Jury consider—buzz a second*]

FOREMAN: [*Rises*] Yes, your Honor, we agree with you. The prisoner is innocent, dirty face or not, and we recommend the library users deal more gently with him and help him keep his face clean.

JUDGE: Superb! Score is 1-0 in disfavor of the library. Next. [*Raps loudly*]

[*Mr. Magazines and Mr. Boys' Life exeunt between the two officers*]

CLERK: The next case is the Library versus Miss Chewing Gum. Charged with excessive locomotion of the jaws, causing strange and unseemly noises in the library.

[*Officers return with* MISS CHEWING GUM *between them*]

CLERK: Bring on the witness!

[*Enter* MRS. LIBRARIAN JONES, *looking distressed*]

CLERK: Do you swear, and all that?

MRS. LIBRARIAN JONES: [*with spirit*] I do if I must! [*Reporters giggle*]

MISS C. G.: Yeah!

D. A.: Your name?

MRS. L. J.: It's posted on the door—

D. A.: [*wearily*] All right! Where were you [*Points finger at her impressively*] on the afternoon of April 10, 1941 at 3 P.M.? [*Time can be suited as desired*]

MRS. L. J.: In the closet sorting pictures. I was expecting the Bulletin Board Committee.

D. A.: What made you think Miss C. G. was present in your sanctum sanctorum?

MRS. L. J.: I heard a snapping noise and smelled an odor of wintergreen.

A. D.: I object! The odor might have been Crystomints.

MRS. L. J.: Don't you tell me that I don't know bubble gum!

JUDGE: [*Comes to from nodding*] Now, that's a good one. Ha-Ha-Ha! [*Laughs heartily. No one else laughs— look at Judge surprised. Judge raps*] Order I say [*No one is out of order but himself*] Hum—Hum [*Pulls himself up to his dignity*] Go on! Go on! Fiddlesticks and golf sticks! Will I never get to my fishing? [*Outside—off stage—cow moos*]

75

JUDGE: Drat Bossie! I told her to stay home. [*looking off right*] Go home, Bossie, go home! [*Cow moos in distance*]

REPORTERS: [*Chant*] There was a cow who came to court, Hey de diddle dee. She certainly didn't hadn't ought, Hey de diddle O.

JUDGE: [*Raps*] Order! If I get mad I'll clear the court. This is no place for choric speech.

D. A.: Continue, Mrs. Librarian Jones, now the Judge has had his fun. [*Glares at Judge. Judge looks down over his glasses at him, strokes his beard*]

MRS. L. J.: I was forced to leave my pictures (and what librarian likes to leave her pictures) and tell Miss Chewing Gum such unseemly actions of the jaws were forbidden in the library. I tried to be polite but at the same time make it clear that she just wasn't wanted in the library—in the library, indeed! [*indignantly*]

D. A.: Yes—yes, go on please—this gets interesting.

JUDGE: [*aside*] Interesting—fiddlesticks!

D. A.: Go on. Judge, I don't like your interruptions if I may say so.

JUDGE: Ha! Got you riled, have I?

MRS. L. J.: Miss Chewing Gum objected.

JUDGE: Fuss and feathers—somebody's always objecting.

MRS. L. J.: [*coldly*] *As* I was saying, I was forced to use violence.

D. A.: What kind, may I ask?

MRS. L. J.: Yes, you may ask. I said "You ought to be ashamed. In the ninth grade—chewing bubble gum in the library where you're not wanted. Get into the waste basket at once." Thereupon she called two friends, Mr. Black Jack and Mr. Beech Nut, who had been lurking, lu—rking in the back of the room, to come to her aid. Why, I got stuck up!

[*Reporters and jury laugh*]

D. A.: No doubt about that.

JUDGE: Order—I see no cause for mirth.

A. D.: I can sympathize with you—poor thing. I've been stuck up myself.

D. A.: I can believe that!

A. D.: I see you're all against my client. I don't seem to have any case.

JUDGE: Right you are! Up and at it jury! Guilty or not— that's *your* job—golf's mine!

[*Moment's silence—jury conferring*]

JUDGE: Verdict, knaves! I can't stay here all day. Rise, culprit.

[*Miss Chewing Gum rises*]

FOREMAN: [*Rises*] Your honor, we find the prisoner guilty as charged, of being in the library against the rules of any respectable library and recommend eternal banishment.

JUDGE: Fine! Now we're getting somewhere. Score is tied. Two innings one to one. [*Bangs gavel loudly*] Next! [*Exeunt Miss Chewing Gum and Mrs. Librarian Jones with officers*]

CLERK: Next case is "The Library versus Mr. Common Nuisance."

JUDGE: Remember—it's the Attorney for the Defense's turn. Let's be fair, this is a court of law and order. [*All shout "sure"*]

A. D.: [*Rises, shakes his own hands above his head*] Thanks a million. Officers, bring in Mr. Common Nuisance and Mr. Wandering Boy. [*Two officers return with* MR. WANDERING BOY *and* MR. COMMON NUISANCE]

CLERK: Do you boys swear, etc., etc.?

MR. WANDERING BOY }
MR. COMMON NUISANCE } [*together*] Oh—yeah!

A. D.: [*addressing Mr. Common Nuisance*] Name, please?

77

Mr. C. N.: [*sulkily*] You know my name and Wandering Boy's, too.

A. D.: All right, if you must be disagreeable. Now, tell the court what you have to say in defense of the prisoner.

Mr. W. B.: Don't know's I can. Know him too well.

Mr. C. N.: Squealer! [*Scowls at him*]

A. D.: Take over, District Attorney. Can't be my witness. Let's change—

D. A.: I wanted to get at this—Thanks, old boy. Now, for the truth. How well do you know Mr. Common Nuisance, Wandering Boy?

Mr. W. B.: Birds of feather—if you know what I mean. He bothers the library all right. Say [*confidentially*] we have a grand time. We annoy the librarian and study teachers, the pupils, and the books, make strange noises, wander all over, throw papers on the floor after crumpling them as loudly as possible, scrape our feet, put them in the chairs, squeak the chairs and mutter. Oh—he's Common Nuisance, all right. He's proud of it and I'm his pal. We never study or read—that's for sissies— you ought to see our funny pictures, too.

D. A.: Proud of it, huh—well, I guess that's proof enough even for the jury.
[*Jury looks wise and attentive—any business desirable may be worked in for the jury at any time*]

Judge: We've got *him* dead to rights. How's the score? Oh! Yes—One to One—Ha! Ha! Ha! [*Laughs*] We'll change that shortly. Not that I like to influence the jury. Odd's bones—got to get out of here—I'm getting behind on my knitting. Consider—the twelve of you. [*Judge stands—stretches, sits regretfully. Jury considers. A. D. paces up and down, looking hopeless*]

Foreman: [*Rises*] Attention—please. We find the prisoner *very guilty* and recommend some lectures on citizenship in a democratic place like the library.

78

[*Exeunt Wandering Boy and Common Nuisance escorted by officers*]

JUDGE: [*addressing audience*] Capital! Score is two to one in favor of the library. Exciting isn't it? [*Bangs with gavel*] Next!

CLERK: Next case is "The Library versus Miss Figgetts Gossip" charged with disturbing the library in the nth degree. Officers, bring in Miss Figgetts Gossip and her witness, Miss Rattle Trap.

[*Officers bring in* MISS FIGGETTS GOSSIP *and* MISS RATTLE TRAP]

A. D.: [*jumping up*] Beat you that time. It's my turn. [*D. A. looks angry*]

CLERK: [*rising hastily*] No, you don't. They've got to swear.

MISS FIGGETTS GOSSIP: Horrors—I can't do that.

CLERK: Tell the truth, chatterbugs!

MISS FIGGETTS GOSSIP ⎱ : If possible, certainly. [*Miss F. G.*
MISS RATTLE TRAP ⎰   *sits—figits—twists handkerchief*]

A. D.: [*to Miss R. T.*] Where do you live?

MISS R. T.: [*tossing head*] Oh! I get around.

A. D.: Be explicit.

MISS R. T.: All over the school.

A. D.: Do you spend much time in the library?

MISS R. T.: Oh—yes—I love "liberries." I go up to meet my friends and talk things over. [*Giggles*] I know plenty, too. We have *such* fun!

A. D.: You'd better not tell.

D. A.: You keep out of this. [*To Miss R. T. sarcastically*] Of course, you don't hinder the work of the library? [*A. D. sits—dejectedly*]

MISS R. T.: Piffle! We don't care about that. We have such important things to say.

D. A.: More important, I suppose [*very icily*] than Latin, Algebra or reference work? You get a good mark in gossip?

Miss R. T.: Oh! Yes—it comes under general information. We have lovely times collecting it, too. I'm trying for Walter Winchell's program. Well—*sometimes* we manage to do a little Latin—

A. D.: That's right. There's an old college adage "Don't let your studies interfere with your good times."

D. A.: Down, I say [*pointing to A. D.'s chair*]
[*A. D. sits again but pleased with himself*]

Miss R. T.: Yes, indeedy!

D. A.: By the way, you and Miss Figgetts Gossip are friends, aren't you?

Miss R. T.: [*impressively*] Yes, indeedy, like twins.

D. A.: That's what *I* thought.

A. D.: That's great! I'll rest my case, folks. This is easy, folks, proving my client not guilty. Look upon her sweet, innocent, young face, [*Miss F. G. flutters her handkerchief and wipes her eyes*] and ask yourself if you can convict such a defenseless young creature? [*addressing the jury*] Where's your chivalry?

Juryman: Please, I haven't it!

A. D.: You may take over, Mr. Smart District Attorney.

Judge: Stenographer strike the word "smart" from the records. Maybe he isn't.
[*Stenographer bangs typewriter keys*]

D. A.: Friends, countrymen, and those who came with you —I am determined to break this witness. To wit [*Turns sharply on Miss R. T.*] and whereas, furthermore and aforesaid—[*silence*]—[*Points close up to her face*] Answer me this one. Are you justified in annoying the library in the nth degree? Yea or nay?

Miss R. T.: [*avoiding the issue*] Well, really now, I don't think—

D. A.: [*interrupting quickly and sarcastically*] There, fellow citizens, you have it in a nutshell [*Points at Miss R. T.*] Behold, you *never* think. Ladies and Gentlemen, the witness admits *she never thinks!* What a state of affairs in a library! What a too, most pitiful state, I say. I appeal to you as democrats and republicans to realize that this witness never thinks. If Miss R. T. never thinks the logic is all too clear in this case; think you Miss F. G. does? My friends, one and one make two— higher math. teaches that. One is Miss R. T., two is Miss F. G. and that proves that neither of them think. [*to the reporters*] Hey, 4th Estate—get this! It's going to be my best speech.

REPORTERS: [*together*] That's what you think.

JUDGE: Keep your seats for this [*Is all attention—cups ear —adjusts glasses*]

D. A.: The gossip people do lives after them—their knowledge of Latin is oft forgotten with their bones. The evil of not thinking is gossip. Mark this well, jury, and bring in a verdict of black, b—lack guilt. [*Wipes brow with large red handkerchief*]

JUDGE: Here, here—that's my speech. Get ye hence, jury.

CLERK: Excuse, please, but are you playing Shakespeare?

JUDGE: Be quiet or I can't excuse you.

[*Jury debates a second—silence*]

JUDGE: [*impatiently*] Well, well, hum, a hum—come, come —what's the good news. Got to fix up the score.

FOREMAN: "It's an ill wind"—not good news. She's guilty —b—lack guilty as charged. We recommend Miss Rattle Trap and Miss Figgetts Gossip and Company think more and talk less.

[*Miss R. T. and Miss F. G. exeunt between officers— shamefaced—wiping eyes*]

JUDGE: Well and now—good, and all that sort of thing. Score's three to one in favor of the library. Get on now. Got to get to my tennis!

CLERK: Next case. "Library versus Mr. Overdue Books" charged with negligence in the most expensive degree. Officers do your stuff.

[*Officers return with* MR. OVERDUE BOOKS *and* MISS DUE DATE]

CLERK: [*wearily*] Swear—you two.

MR. OVERDUE BOOKS: Sure—glad to oblige—anything, anytime.

MISS DUE DATE: Most truthfully, but Mr. Overdue Books never lets me keep my word. [*glaring at Mr. O. B.*]

D. A.: Hah, conspiracy!

A. D.: My turn, Pal—

[*D. A. sits, dejectedly. Takes bite of apple*]

A. D.: Names—never mind, I know. [*Addressing Miss D. D.*] Tell me, where do you live.

MISS D. D.: [*timidly*] On a pink slip in the back of all circulating library books.

A. D.: What do you do for a living?

MISS D. D.: I have a very important position. I show the date when books are due in the library.

D. A.: I object! Your Honor, at least I'd like to say something.

A. D.: Oh! All right, but it's rude to interrupt.

JUDGE: Objection sustained. Proceed Mr. Sneed—I mean District Attorney to you.

[*A. D. sits down, dejectedly*]

D. A.: Miss Due Date, how is it, if you do your job so well, that Mr. Overdue Books is charged with this crime? I think you must be careless.

MISS D. D.: [*Sniffs*] Careless, indeed. You think entirely wrong. [*Stamps her feet*] I'm like the radio.

D. A.: I'll bite. How's that?

82

MISS D. D.: Simple enough. If you don't turn on a radio you don't hear anything.

D. A.: Yes, yes, be explicit. That doesn't sound like a good joke.

MISS D. D.: I mean just this: If Mr. Overdue Books doesn't look at me he doesn't know when his book is due.

D. A.: Phooey, and yet again phooey.

A. D.: I object. That's perfectly relevant, material, and right to the point.

JUDGE: [*sleepily*] Sustained!

A. D.: Now, I'd like to establish some reasons why Mr. Overdue Books is innocent.

D. A.: Can't be done, brother!

JUDGE: Quiet, please!

A. D.: [*Glares at D. A.*] Continue Miss Due Date.
[*Mr. O. B. looks more and more beaten*]

MISS D. D.: My friends, The Overdue Committee, Mrs. Librarian Jones, Home Room Librarians, and teachers do everything in their power to help Mr. O. B. but he's a careless fellow.

A. D.: I agree. That's enough. I'm getting hungry [*Takes sandwich out of his pocket and places it on his desk. Looks at it longingly*]

JUDGE: So are we all—all getting hungry. Who gets it this time? Jury, your duty is clear.

JURY: [*not waiting to consider, all together chant*] He is guilty, he is guilty, fine him, punish him, stop his wicked deeds.

JUDGE: Very pretty. I am with you. Score is four to one in favor of the library. Glad I'm score keeper. Gives me something to do.
[*Exeunt Mr. O. B. and Miss D. D. escorted by officers. Mr. O. B. is very dejected, Miss D. D. looks triumphant*]

JUDGE: [*Bangs with gavel*] Next!

CLERK: [*shouting*] Bring in the next victim. "Library versus Mr. Non-Fiction" charged with loitering habitually in the library. Bring in the witness Mr. Biography, also. Let's make this snappy.

JUDGE: Atta boy!

[*Officers return with* MR. NON-FICTION *and* MR. BIOGRAPHY]

CLERK: You'd better say you'll tell the truth, it's a bore and I'm heartily tired of mentioning it, but it's in the rules.

MR. NON-FICTION ⎱ [*together*] I swear, but I don't ap-
MR. BIOGRAPHY ⎰ prove of swearing.

D. A.: Come, give me a chance at this. I can't hold this chair down any longer. Piffle, I know your names. [*Addressing Mr. B.*] Where do you live?

[*Mr. N. F. sits down, wearily in prisoner's chair*]

MR. B.: In plain sight in the library and I'm tired of it. Got my number? 920-928 in case you'd like to know. I demand justice. Oh! for a Zola—oh!—for Portia—do I get justice or not?

D. A.: I ask the questions around here.

MR. B.: You can't do this to me and Mr. Non-Fiction. I have rheumatism from lack of exercise and it pleases the court to call it loitering.

D. A.: The court is not interested in your ailments. You'll be telling us about your operation next.

MR. B.: I was getting to that. I was in Barnard's Hospital three weeks and got new red covers and bright gold markings and still no one pays any attention to me. It's shameful. Sport Fiction, Mystery Story, Historical Novel and Career Book get all the exercise.

A. D.: I object.

JUDGE: Objection sustained.

A. D.: I was thinking—

JUDGE: Good idea. It's your turn. The District Attorney's had his and he doesn't get anywhere.

A. D.: Now, Judge [*smiling at the judge amiably*], if you can't sit through a court session without feeling the need of exercise, golf shall we say, [*Judge nods and smiles approval*] how can we expect Mr. Biography and Mr. Non-Fiction to enjoy loitering on the shelves day in, day out, week in, and week out, while their arch enemies Sport Fiction, Mystery Story, Historical Novel, etc., have all the fun?

JUDGE: You've got us there for fair!

D. A.: I'm lost! I'm lost! Everyone is against me. Boo hoo. [*Weeps into large blue handkerchief. Mr. B. looks happy—as does Mr. N. F.*]

MR. B.: Now we're getting sympathy—maybe justice, who knows? How about justice for all my relatives? Mr. Science, Miss Poetry, Mr. Art, Miss Music, and Mr. Travel. They could use some circulation. They would rather be out in the world than loitering on the shelves, as you choose to call it.

A. D.: You've explained things just dandy. Jury, you must agree with me that Mr. Biography has proved Mr. Non-Fiction entirely innocent. He needs helping hands, he wants to go to homes and have a look around—so do his friends. This fiction rabble has been having it all their own way.

JUDGE: Forevermore! Couldn't do better myself. Jury, do as you please. You know I'm never prejudiced. It's about ten minutes to my golf now, I hope—I hope!
[*Jury deliberates a second*]

FOREMAN: Your honor, the prisoner is innocent. No doubt about it. The guilty ones are below in the court [*Faces audience—seriously—points at audience*] You and you and you are the guilty ones and we, the jury, sentence you to read one book of Mr. Non-Fiction and his relatives, a week until the cramps are all out of them. They need their circulation pepped up or they'll be cripples!

JUDGE: Bully. Score is four to two in favor of the library. [*Exeunt Mr. N. F. and Mr. B. with officers, looking well pleased with everything*]

MR. B.: [*as he is leaving, shouts*] Justice at last! [*Judge bangs gavel*]

CLERK: Last case! "Library versus Miss Shelvers" charged with exceeding the speed limit with Mr. Book Truck. Officers, bring in Miss Shelvers and Mr. Book Truck. [*Enter* MISS SHELVERS *and* MR. BOOK TRUCK *with officers*]

CLERK: If you don't know by this time you have to tell the truth, you never will. I'm not going to tell you.

MISS SHELVERS
MR. BOOK TRUCK } [*together*] I do.

D. A.: *I'm* getting in on *this*. Name [*addressing Mr. B. T.*]

MR. B. T.: Book Truck, thought everybody knew it.

D. A.: It's just a form, have to ask you or it isn't legal. Now, tell the court in your own words what the trouble is.

MR. B. T.: My job is to carry the books back to the shelves. I heard the librarian say, "Take it easy, you're not going to a fire."

D. A.: Aha! Enough, that proves my case. Fire truck, indeed, in the library! Hum!

JUDGE: Exactly, though far be it from me to prejudice anybody. Jury, your verdict!

JURY: [*all shout*] Guilty!

MR. B. T.: Well, turn my wheels and set me going!

FOREMAN: We sentence the prisoner to a speed not to exceed a walking step—no more fire truck business in the library.

JUDGE: Now, that's just the way I feel about it. Thank goodness, I can get to my golf. Score is five to two in favor of the library and "I'm happy about the whole thing." [*aside*] Now to redeem myself. [*Stands up—swells—strokes beard*] Friends, you have heard the sentences against these prisoners. It is not only my duty, but yours as well, to see that they are carried out. The library is a democratic institution for all the pupils and should be treated with respect at all times. [*Jury, reporters, clerk and stenographer applaud by clapping*] "The Guilty Ones" are the patrons who misuse poor Mr. Magazines, who disregard Mr. Biography, who annoy like Miss Gossip, and Miss Chewing Gum, who are careless like Mr. Overdue Books. Let us beware [*Points impressively at audience*] that no hint of guilt fall further upon us—the library users. Now, everybody— [*addressing those on stage*] the library yell. [*Judge leads—all join in*]

ALL: Library, Library, Rah, Rah, Rah!
No more overdues
No more fines.
Magazines in their places
On the shelves more empty spaces.
Library, Library, Rah, Rah, Rah!

Treasure in the Garret

by

Helen C. Sill

No royalty charged for production.

Treasure in the Garret

CHARACTERS:

> MARY } cousins visiting Grandmother and Uncle Will at
> JANE } Grandmother's home near Cambridge, Massachusetts
> JACK, aged twelve—Mary's brother
> TOM, aged eleven—Jane's brother
> JOHN NEWBERY—bookseller and publisher. He is dressed in an
>   eighteenth-century drab brown suit. He wears spectacles
> PAGE—wears a purple suit with ruff
> MOTHER HUBBARD—in early eighteenth-century print dress with
>   mob cap
> DOG TRAY—child dressed to look like a dog
> GOODY TWO SHOES—in an early eighteenth-century costume
> TEACHER—Puritan costume
> MARY ELLEN, JEDEDIAH, and COLONIAL CHILDREN—in colonial
>   costume of blue or grey
> UNCLE WILL—in present-day dress

SCENE: The action of this play takes place in the attic of an old
Massachusetts farm house. By the scanty light admitted through
a rain-spattered window there are seen beneath the cob-webbed
rafters two or three old trunks. At the right is an old delapi-
dated screen. As the curtain opens, enter MARY and JANE,
about eleven and twelve years old.

MARY: Why are rainy days so much nicer on a farm than
in the city?

JANE: Maybe it is because apartments don't have garrets.

MARY: No, nor room to keep old things. Mother even
threw away my teddy bear because she thought it was
old junk. He was a little dirty but I didn't mind.

JANE: [holding up key] Let's see which trunk this key fits.
[Tries locks of one or more before she finds the right
one. Opens it and discloses a quantity of old clothes]
Here, it is this one.

MARY: Phew! Smell the moth balls.

JANE: Hold your nose and let's dress up.

MARY: Here, you put on that petticoat and I'll take this one.

JANE: I want that blue skirt.

MARY: Tie this sash, please.

JANE: You had better put on a waist first.

MARY: All right. Oh, where did you get that *beau-ti-ful* cape?

JANE: Look at this hat.

MARY: You look funny.

JANE: [*Crosses stage with a flourish*] I don't either. I'm a grand lady going to a party.

MARY: [*making a sweeping bow*] I'll call the carriage, madame. [*Starts for the door but hears footsteps on the stairs*] Oh, bother! Here come Tom and Jack. Now they'll spoil all the fun. Why couldn't they stay out in the barn?

JANE: Let's hide. If they see us dressed up, they'll laugh. Lock the trunk so they can't get anything to play with and maybe they will go away.

[*Girls lock trunk and hide behind screen. Boys enter*]

JACK: Good. No one here. I wonder where the girls are.

TOM: [*in contemptuous tone*] Probably playing with dolls.

JACK: Do you suppose we can find that treasure Uncle Will told about last night? I wonder what it is.

[*Screen gives a hitch nearer*]

TOM: He said that he used to see it often when he was a boy but then he did not know how valuable it was.

JACK: And he said it was in one of these trunks. Boy, I'd like to find it! Let's see which it is.

[*Boys inspect trunks and screen moves closer to afford a better view for the girls*]

Hello, this trunk is locked. Is that one?

TOM: Yes.

JACK: 'Spose Grandma would let us have the key? I've got a hunch that it is in that one.

[*Points to the trunk for which the girls have the key*]

TOM: Let's go ask her.

[*Exit boys. Girls come out from their hiding place*]

JANE: Push that trunk against the door so they can't get in. Quick! Now let's find the treasure.

MARY: What do you suppose it is?

JANE: Pearls, maybe,—or diamonds.

MARY: Or pieces of eight like Captain Kidd buried.

JANE: Or cloth of gold.

[*Girls dig in trunk and pull out dresses which they strew about the floor. In the bottom they discover some old books*]

Oh, Mary, look. We have the wrong trunk. There is no treasure here—only old musty books.

[*Enter* JOHN NEWBERY]

JOHN NEWBERY: Are you so sure?

MARY AND JANE: [*Jump back in surprise*] Oh, who are you?

NEWBERY: I am a man whom every boy and girl should thank.

JANE: Do you play dress-up too?

NEWBERY: No, Mistress. This is my work-a-day garb. My name is John Newbery. Perhaps you may have heard of me.

MARY: Are you the man who gives a prize for children's books?

NEWBERY: I am the man in whose honor the prize is given. I lived in England two hundred years ago and published books especially for boys and girls. People sometimes call me the "Father of Children's Literature." The prize you mentioned is given by the American Library Association each year for the best book for children published during the current year.

I came because you said there is no treasure in this trunk. Look! [*Picks up "Babees Boke"*] I will try to show you the value of these. Now there are two ways of making a book come alive: first, by reading it—any one can do that—or by really seeing it. Shall we try?

GIRLS: Oh, yes! [*Newbery holds up book and blows dust off. (Fullers earth makes excellent dust)*]

[*Enter* PAGE]

PAGE: You sent for me, Sir?

NEWBERY: I did. Tell these young ladies what is in your book.

PAGE: My book is called the *Babees Boke* and tells how boys should behave. Noblemen used it in the time of Columbus. I will read you some of the rules: "Speak when thou art spoken to. Shuffle not thy feet, lean not against posts, neither scratch thyself in public. Wipe thy mouth clean after eating and see that thy cup is kept spotless that others may drink from it. Always wash thy hands *after* a meal is over."

[*Exit Page*]

JANE: Those rules are not so queer except the last one. Mother tells us to wash our hands before we eat.

NEWBERY: [*rummaging in trunk*] I see you have one of my Chap Books. I published these to fit small hands. Let's hear from this one.

MARY: How small it is!

JANE: I can scarcely read it. Were the pages always so yellow?

NEWBERY: Not quite. The color comes with age but the print, I fear, was always bad. We thought it very good two hundred years ago.

[*Blows dust from book and* OLD MOTHER HUBBARD *and* DOG TRAY *enter*]

JANE: It is Mother Hubbard and her dog, Tray.

MARY: Mother Hubbard, were you really in such a small book?

MOTHER HUBBARD: Indeed I was but I never knew why.

NEWBERY: I can tell you. When I printed your book, I put one verse and a picture on a page. When I made a thick book, I put in a great many verses, but when I made a thin one, I left out some. That is why there are so many versions of your poems. Won't you please read a few of the verses, Mary?

MARY: [*Mother Hubbard and Dog Tray pantomime the action as Mary reads*]

"Old Mother Hubbard
Went to the Cupboard,
To get her poor dog a bone;
But when she came there,
The cupboard was bare,
And so the poor dog had none.

"She went to the baker's
To buy him some bread
But when she came back
The poor dog was dead.

"She went to the joiner's
To buy him a coffin
But when she came back
The poor dog was laughing.

"She took a clean dish
To get him some tripe
But when she came back
He was smoking a pipe.

"The dame made a curtsy;
The dog made a bow;
The dame said, 'Your servant,'
The dog said, 'Bow, wow.' "

[*Mother Hubbard and dog exeunt*]

NEWBERY: Here is another of my books—*Mistress Goody Two Shoes.*

JANE: Was that a book for girls?

NEWBERY: Yes, it was one of the very first. Have you read it?

MARY: No, but I saw a book by that name in the library the other day.

NEWBERY: I understand that boys and girls still read it. I must tell my friend, Oliver Goldsmith. He is really much annoyed because people are not certain that he wrote it. [*admonishingly*] Remember—always sign your name if you want credit for your work. Come, Goody Two Shoes.

[*Blows dust from the book.* GOODY TWO SHOES *enters*]

GOODY TWO SHOES: You called, Sir?

NEWBERY: Yes, I want you to meet my twentieth century friends. Jane and Mary, may I present Goody Two Shoes?

JANE AND MARY: How do you do?

GOODY TWO SHOES: [*curtsying*] It is a pleasure to meet you.

JANE: Won't you tell us about yourself.

GOODY TWO SHOES: Alas, I have had such a distressing life!—but now all is well. Instead of going barefoot as I used to do, I now have two good shoes. That is where I got my name.

[*Holds up shoes to view. Puts them back on and dances an English country dance. Exits*]

NEWBERY: [*Takes out horn book*] Still more treasure. A Horn Book.

MARY: It doesn't look like a book.

NEWBERY: But it is a kind of book—and the very one from which your great-great-great grandmother learned her A-B-C's. [*Blows dust from book*] Look, there she is now!

96

[COLONIAL CHILDREN *and* TEACHER *enter*]

JANE: Which is our great-great-great grandmother?
[*Newbery points as Colonial children form a line to recite before their teacher*]

TEACHER: Mary Ellen, you may recite.

MARY ELLEN: A-a, B-b, C-c, Ab, eb, ib, ob, ub, yb, Ba, be, bi, bo, bu, by.

TEACHER: Jedediah, toe the line. What is the first commandment?

JEDEDIAH: Thou shalt have no other gods before me.

TEACHER: What is the third commandment, class?

CLASS: Remember the Sabbath day to keep it holy.

NEWBERY: Would you be so kind as to have your pupils sing from this book which I have found.

TEACHER: Gladly. We often sing from this book on Sundays.
[*Class sings: "Let Us With a Gladsome Mind," by John Milton. Psalm 136*]

CLASS: "Let us with a gladsome mind
          Praise the Lord, for he is kind:
          CHORUS:
          "For his mercies aye endure,
          Ever faithful, ever sure.

          "Who by his all-commanding might,
          Did fill the new-made world with light:
          (CHORUS)
          "All living creatures he doth feed;
          And with full hand supplies their need:
          (CHORUS)
          "Let us, therefore, warble forth,
          His mighty majesty and worth."
          (CHORUS)
[*Exeunt*]

MARY: What is that song book? It looks a little like a Bible.

NEWBERY: It is a part of the Bible in verse. This is the Bay Psalm Book. It was the first book to be printed in the United States. It was published in Cambridge, Massachusetts in 1640. There are only eleven copies known to be in existence.

JANE: This is all very interesting, but where is the treasure?

NEWBERY: To possess old books is treasure in itself—but if you mean money—this book is worth its weight in gold. One just like it sold for $1,025 a few years ago.

GIRLS: Really! Then we have found the treasure!

NEWBERY: Listen. I hear someone coming. I must go. Good-day.

JANE AND MARY: Good day, Sir.

[*Boys are heard mounting the stairs. Girls turn to greet them triumphantly and Newbery exits.* BOYS *enter*]

TOM: Where did you get the rigs? Gee, you look funny!

JANE: Never mind how we look. Just wait until you hear the news.

MARY: So you think you are going to find treasure. Too bad! You are just too late. We have it already.

JACK: Where?

JANE: [*holding up Bay Psalm Book*] Here.

TOM: Huh! That's all girls know about treasure. Nothing but a musty old book. Ugh!

JANE: But this *is* the treasure.

JACK: Who said so?

MARY: John Newbery.

JACK: Who's he?

JANE: Never mind, Mary. He wouldn't understand.

TOM: Get out of my way and let me look.

MARY: You won't find it.

TOM: I will.

MARY: You won't.

TOM: I will too.

MARY: You won't so.

[*Voices rise until hubbub is heard and* UNCLE WILL *enters*]

UNCLE WILL: What is all this row?

JACK: It is those silly girls. They call *that* treasure.

MARY: We heard the boys talking about treasure so we searched until we found it.

UNCLE WILL: [*Takes book, examines it carefully and—in surprise*] So it is, girls, but how under the sun did you know it?

JANE: John Newbery told us.

UNCLE WILL: John Newbery! Did he tell you? You know —once on a rainy day just like this when I was your age, he came and told me too.

TOM: [*mystified*] Uncle Will, what is this all about?

UNCLE WILL: I will explain it all to you after dinner— that is all about who John Newbery was and how valuable this book really is.

MARY: Are we going to sell this book, Uncle Will?

UNCLE WILL: No, Mary, for while the book may be worth a great deal of money, it is much more important to us because one of our ancestors owned it and sang from it long ago.

Boys, perhaps I can show you something of what the girls have seen. When the wind is in the east, blow on the southwest corner of a very old book which has not been dusted for at least twenty years, and something is sure to happen. [*Blows and all characters reappear and bow*]

[CURTAIN]

99

The Olde Book Shoppe

by

Teresa M. Compitello

The first seven scenes of this play are reproduced, with some changes, from Rosa Sasloe's *The Book Shop,* now out of print. Permission was granted by Little, Brown & Co., Charles Scribner's Sons, D. Appleton-Century, and F. S. Crofts & Co. to use the quotations from *Ramona* by Helen Hunt Jackson, *The Yearling* by Marjorie Rawlings, *Florence Nightingale* by Laura E. Richards, and the Lincoln-Douglas debates (Commager's *Documents of American History*).

No royalty charged for production. Anyone wishing additional information on the sound effects used in the play should inquire of Miss Teresa M. Compitello, Librarian, Mynderse Academy, Seneca Falls, N.Y.

(The scenes are illustrative of books for children
of kindergarten age up through grade twelve)

Scenery :
An old-fashioned book shop may be constructed by putting a
door frame in center back stage with regular stage curtains on
either side. On one side of the door, put an old-fashioned lantern,
and a dimly lighted sign, "The Olde Book Shoppe." On the other
side, a poster may be put to represent a window display of several
books.

Shadow effects, as needed in "My Shadow" and in "Emperor
Jones" may be produced by attaching a sheet to a ceiling front
curtain and closing the front stage curtains to width of sheet. All
stage lights should be turned off, and a bright spotlight worked on
sheet from center back, behind sheet. The height of persons may
be adjusted by moving the light back and forth.

A public address system should be connected so that the loud-
speakers are at either end of front stage, and the microphone and
control are backstage.

The chorus, pianist, book reviewers (or "Voice"), and others
taking part in speaking part of program, are backstage.

In order to keep the play moving, it is advisable to have the
pianist play the music for the preceding scenes while the changes
are taking place backstage. For instance, at the close of the first
scene, the pianist plays "The Big Brown Bear" until Scene II is
ready and the voice begins speaking. With the pianist backstage,
it is easy to signal her to stop whenever the speaker is ready.

The play includes characters from all grades and lasts about
45 minutes. However, any of the scenes may be omitted without
detracting from the play.

For books such as Mother Goose that do not have an author,
the pages may carry a poster bearing the number of the grade for
which book is intended.

Cast of Characters :

Scene I. Mother Goose Nursery Rhymes   Kindergarten
    Little Bo Peep
    Simple Simon
    Pieman
    Old Mother Hubbard
    Wee Willie Winkie

Scene II. The Three Bears   Grade One
    Goldilocks

103

SCENE III. A Child's Garden of Verses   GRADE TWO
    SMALL BOY
SCENE IV. Pinocchio   GRADE THREE
    PINOCCHIO
    GEPPETTO
SCENE V. King Arthur and His Knights   GRADE FOUR
    KING ARTHUR
    PRINCESS GUINEVERE
SCENE VI. Hansel and Gretel   GRADE FIVE
    HANSEL
    GRETEL
SCENE VII. Rip Van Winkle   GRADE SIX
    RIP VAN WINKLE
    VILLAGERS
    INDIANS
SCENE VIII. David Copperfield   GRADE SEVEN
    DAVID COPPERFIELD
    MR. MICAWBER
    MRS. MICAWBER AND CHILDREN
    MR. QUINION
SCENE IX. The Three Musketeers   GRADE EIGHT
    THREE MUSKETEERS
SCENE X. Ramona   GRADE NINE
    YOUNG INDIAN MAIDEN
    YOUNG INDIAN BOY
    OTHER INDIANS IF DESIRED
SCENE XI. Florence Nightingale   GRADE TEN
    ENGLISH GIRL OF 1820, SEVEN YEARS OLD
    GIRL OF SEVENTEEN
    LITTLE BOY
    YOUNG WOMAN IN NURSE'S COSTUME
    WOUNDED SOLDIERS
SCENE XII. Abe Lincoln in Illinois   GRADE ELEVEN
    ABRAHAM LINCOLN
    STEPHEN DOUGLAS
    AUDIENCE
SCENE XIII. The Yearling   GRADE TWELVE
    JODY AND HIS FAWN

TWO PAGES (wearing dark suits with brass buttons and pill box hats)
BOOK REVIEWER, who does all the talking through a microphone backstage
BOY to work sound effects
GROUP of about eight from Glee Club
PIANIST

The Olde Book Shoppe

SCENE I. MOTHER GOOSE
Kindergarten

CHORUS: [*sings*]

> Good evening to you,
> Good evening to you,
> Good evening, dear audience,
> And how do you do?

[*Enter* PAGES *at center, through nearly closed curtains, with posters bearing title of book and author*]

VOICE: [*from backstage*] "Mother Goose." This name familiar in connection with nursery rhymes is of uncertain origin. *Tales of Mother Goose* was the title of a series of French stories as early as 1697.

Mother Goose Melodies was the title of some nursery rhymes written by Elizabeth Goose of Boston in 1719. Another set of rhymes was published for children by Newbery, about the middle of the 18th century, again with the heading, *Mother Goose Melodies*. In 1826 appeared *Mother Goose's Quarto* in Boston.

Thus, the name has become closely connected with nursery lore, by what process we know not. However, they were brought down to us, and all the children delight in "Mother Goose Nursery Rhymes." We hope you will like those we present.

[*Curtain opens. Pages walk to opposite sides of stage and remain there until scene is finished*]

105

[*Enter* SIMPLE SIMON *(short narrow trousers, flowing bow tie, with bright colored blouse, feather in hat) and* PIEMAN *(in baker's suit—white duck or street clothes with white apron, and small white baker's cap, carrying tray of pies suspended from neck; pies may be made of cotton with colored paper for fillings, brown for chocolate, yellow for lemon, etc.)*]

VOICE: [*Recites slowly so that characters may act in pantomime*]

> "Simple Simon met a pieman
>   Going to the fair,
> Says Simple Simon to the pieman,
>   'Let me taste your ware.'
>
> "Says the pieman to Simple Simon
>   'Let me see your penny'
> Says Simple Simon to the pieman,
>   "Indeed I have not any.' "

[*As voice finishes, characters take places at right of center door back, to form a balanced group when Mother Goose Rhymes are finished*]

[*Enter* LITTLE BO PEEP *(dressed in simple summer dress, carrying a long shepherd's crook)*]

VOICE:

> "Little Bo Beep has lost her sheep
> And can't tell where to find them.
> Let them alone and they'll come home
> Wagging their tails behind them."

[*She takes place at left of center door back*]

[*Enter* OLD MOTHER HUBBARD *(dressed in old-fashioned woman's dress, with spectacles on nose, and cane for support)*]

106

VOICE:

"Old Mother Hubbard went to the cupboard
    To get her poor dog a bone.
But when she got there the cupboard was bare
    And so the poor dog had none."

[*As voice finishes, she takes place at right of door*]

[*Enter* WEE WILLIE WINKIE *(in night shirt holding burning candle in old candle stick)*]

VOICE:

"Wee Willie Winkie runs through the town,
Upstairs and downstairs in his nightgown,
Rapping at the window, calling through the lock,
'Are the children all in bed for it's now eight
    o'clock.'"

[*Takes place at left of door. As music starts, Pages step back of curtain. Music concludes with chorus singing*]:

"Good evening, dear audience, And how do you do?"

[CURTAIN]

SCENE II.   THE THREE BEARS
Grade One

CHARACTERS: Goldilocks with blonde hair, dressed in frilly summer dress.
MUSIC: "Big Brown Bear" by Zucca.

[*Curtain opens enough to let* PAGES *out the same as in Scene* I]

VOICE: Fairy Tales. Fairy tales have been told for many centuries. Before the time when they were written at all in the form of a book, they were told by word of mouth.

107

Many authors have written these tales that have been handed down through the ages. Grimm is the author of *Household Tales*. Andersen, another prominent writer, wrote the *Andersen's Fairy Tales*. Carroll has given us *Alice's Adventures in Wonderland*, Kingsley, *The Water Babies*. These are the most popular versions of fairy tales among children.

We will show you a scene from "The Three Bears."

[*Curtain full stage*]

[*Enter* GOLDILOCKS, *runs to center of stage looking about cautiously, runs to one side, then another, looking timidly and yet inquisitively about. Discovers bowl of porridge. (Here as well as in other scenes based on fairy tales it is better not to use table or other stage properties, but rather to carry out the idea of the child's make-believe world)*]

[*Goldilocks (as if attention is called to make-believe table) bends over to taste porridge*]

VOICE: [*offstage*] This is too hot—This is too cold—This is just right.

[*Goldilocks looks about for chairs*]

VOICE: This is too hard—This is too soft—This is just right.

[*Goldilocks falls down to indicate the broken chair*]

[*She tries beds*]

VOICE: This is too hard—This is too soft—This is just right.

[*Goldilocks goes to sleep*]

108

[*Chorus backstage sings softly parts of "The Big Brown Bear." While the chorus sings the line, "When all he said was Woof," the Pages step back of curtains and Goldilocks runs off stage*]

[*Curtain closes as pianist continues to play "The Big Brown Bear"*]

SCENE III. A CHILD'S GARDEN OF VERSES

Grade Two

CHARACTER: Small boy

MUSIC: From the song "My Shadow"

The POEM selected: "My Shadow" (Others may be used if preferred)

STAGE: Dark—sheet used with light backstage. Boy stands to produce desired effects.

[*Enter PAGES as before*]

VOICE: Robert Louis Stevenson. Robert Louis Stevenson was born in Edinburgh, November 13, 1850. He entered Edinburgh University intending to become an engineer. He turned his back on this plan, after recovering from a long illness.

Stevenson's bent toward a literary career was encouraged. As a result of his ambition, the following are among his best known works: *The Merry Men, Treasure Island, Dr. Jekyll and Mr. Hyde,* and *A Child's Garden of Verses.*

From the latter book we are showing our interpretation of one of his poems in shadow effects.

[*Light is turned on sheet and Voice recites poem, "My Shadow" as Small Boy acts in pantomime*]

[*Lights on, Pages step back, music and curtain*]

109

SCENE IV. PINOCCHIO
Grade Three

MUSIC: "Funiculi, Funicula."
CHARACTERS: PINOCCHIO (tan cardboard front and back, or khaki-colored suit to give wooden mechanical effect), and GEPPETTO (dressed shabbily as a carpenter in work clothes, with iron gray wig).

[*Enter* PAGES *as before*]

VOICE: "Pinocchio." Carlo Collodi is the author of *Pinocchio*. This book was written for children and has already become a classic. Of all the fairy tales in Italian folklore, this is best known and best loved. It has been translated into many languages and has become a favorite with children in many lands.

Let us introduce the marionette and his maker, Geppetto.

[*Curtain full stage*]

[*Scene discloses* GEPPETTO *at work on his marionette,* PINOCCHIO, *who stands very rigid. While Geppetto hammers nails into the marionette, the sound effect is produced by hammering on a small board in front of the microphone backstage in time to his hammering on stage. As he finishes his last bit of work, he examines Pinocchio critically, trying and smoothing a joint here and there, and testing them again and again (sound for squeaking joints produced by opening and closing a bridle bit snap in front of microphone)*
As he tries his arms, Pinocchio drops them in mechanical fashion. When Geppetto tries his legs, the rogue takes a chance at kicking his maker while his back is turned. But as he turns he smooths some part of the knees with sandpaper. And as he puts the hat on Pinocchio after a few seconds of fond admiration of his handiwork, he steps aside, and Pinocchio takes this

110

opportunity to enjoy his freedom in playful glee, jumping about on the stage in tricky capers. Then just as he approaches his maker, he seizes his wig and runs off stage, with Geppetto after him]

[*Pages return as before, music, curtain*]

SCENE. V. KING ARTHUR AND HIS KNIGHTS
Grade Four

MUSIC: English martial music ("Pomp and Circumstance")

CHARACTERS: GUINEVERE (in gown with train trimmed with three-inch strips of cotton with black painted spots for ermine effect. Her crown is of silver paper on cardboard, with jewels—spots of red, blue, and green paint to give jewel effect). KING ARTHUR (in black suit, made of paper muslin or kid finish cambric, with gray collar and frontispiece to give armor effect. His shield and sword are made of oak tag painted with coat of arms.)

[*PAGES enter as before. They allow a few seconds for audience to see posters and walk to ends of stage*]

[*Curtain opens, the only light is a bright spotlight turned on tableau showing* KING ARTHUR *kneeling before* GUINEVERE, *as she holds sword touching his shoulder*]

VOICE: [*to very soft martial music*] "King Arthur and His Knights" was written to give children an interest in the literature dealing with the great Celtic legend of King Arthur, and to arouse their admiration for the sturdy national virtues of which the English race has always been so proud. Here is just a beautiful picture of King Arthur and Princess Guinevere, whose hand he sought and won.

[*Pages step back, music as curtain is closed*]

111

SCENE VI. HANSEL AND GRETEL
Grade Five

MUSIC: "Hansel and Gretel" by Humperdinck, from opera score.
CHARACTERS: HANSEL and GRETEL (dressed in German peasant costume. Clothes poor but clean, colored patches very prominent)

[*Enter two* PAGES]

VOICE: "Hansel and Gretel." Many years ago there lived in Germany some very happy children. At holiday time their mother wrote pretty plays for them to act. The famous musician and composer, Engelbert Humperdinck, who was their uncle, wrote music for these plays. One of the little plays which he set to music was taken from the old legend "Hansel and Gretel." Everyone liked it so much that Humperdinck transcribed this musical play into the opera known by that name. The opera, "Hansel and Gretel," is as well known to music lovers as the simple story it tells is known to children.

[*Curtain full stage*]

[HANSEL *is working on broom,* GRETEL *knitting. Dramatize part of story beginning with this scene. Children throw work away and decide to play. Hansel tastes of cream in pitcher. Gretel remonstrates with him. She proposes to teach a dance. Chorus backstage sings score as Gretel goes through dance. They hum it as she tries to teach Hansel. He goes through it very awkwardly. The next time through the chorus again sings the score and both dance in step*]

[*Pages exit as before. Music. Curtain closes*]

112

SCENE VII. RIP VAN WINKLE
Grade Six

MUSIC: "Cradle Song" by Brahms.

CHARACTERS: VILLAGERS (use as many as stage will allow in Colonial costumes, as ordinary Dutch settlers. Powdered hair or white wigs) INDIANS: (number left to producer—in brown or tan khaki Indian costumes, or blankets thrown over shoulders, feathered headgear). RIP VAN WINKLE (uncouth dress, long grizzled beard, old gun)

[PAGES *enter*]

VOICE: "Rip Van Winkle." One of the characters of early American literature, which our historian and humorist, Washington Irving, has introduced to the reading public, is Rip Van Winkle. The story of his twenty years' sleep needs no retelling.

Let us set before you a street scene showing Rip Van Winkle's return.

[*Curtain showing street scene*]

[*Groups of* VILLAGERS *are standing about in conversation. Groups of* CHILDREN *are at play. One fellow is passing out handbills to citizens about the election. As they raise hands in pretense of shouting, the actual shouting is done by chorus off stage:* "Election," "Federal," "Democrat," "Liberty," "Rights of Citizens." (Repeat same, thus giving audience time to react to scene) RIP *appears at center back, comes forward and slowly looks about, first at one group and then at another. At first no one notices him, then gradually groups begin to stare at him, children run behind parents for protection, groups band together as they collectively start toward him and then rustle him off the stage*]
[*Pages exit, music, curtain*]

SCENE VIII. DAVID COPPERFIELD
Grade Seven

MUSIC: Any English folk song.

CHARACTERS: MR. MICAWBER, very pompous looking; MRS. MICAW-BER, (in nineteenth-century house dress, of rather faded-looking material); FOUR MICAWBER CHILDREN, including twins; MR. QUINION; DAVID COPPERFIELD in English boy's outfit of Dickens period.

SCENE: Room in the Micawber home showing Mr. Micawber at table reading paper, Mrs. Micawber trying to straighten room as first one child tugs at her apron and then another.

[PAGES *enter*]

VOICE: "David Copperfield" by Charles Dickens was written in 1850. It is acknowledged by authorities to be Dickens' masterpiece and was regarded by Dickens himself as his best work. The hero's experiences relate the author's own early life.

We are depicting a scene from *David Copperfield* at the time David came to make his home with the Micawbers. [*A knock is heard at the door, Mrs. Micawber starts to answer but Mr. Micawber intervenes and goes to the door*] Mr. Quinion introduces David to Mr. Micawber, a man of big words and pompous manners. Mrs. Micawber, in her motherly fashion, is trying to impress David and make him feel at home. The children alternately cling to and hide behind her. David is a stranger there and they are exceedingly shy of him. [*Children gradually come near him, and first one and then another warms up to him*] David welcomes the opportunity to be with other children and with a family as congenial and hospitable as the Micawbers. He proceeds to make himself at home.

[NOTE: *Stage business as indicated in brackets would depend on producer*]

[*Pages exit, music and curtain*]

114

SCENE IX. THE THREE MUSKETEERS
Grade Eight

MUSIC: "March of the Three Musketeers" (from the musical comedy of the same name)

CHARACTERS: THREE MUSKETEERS (dressed in bright colored silk blouses with black velvet capes, large hats with plumes, riding shoes, dark trousers tucked in shoes, swords)

[PAGES *enter*]

VOICE: "The Three Musketeers," written in 1844 by Alexandre Dumas, is a cycle of three romances from youth to age giving an excellent picture of the history of that time (1126-71). Political intrigue, court life, duelling and fighting, form the substance of this novel. With the chorus singing "The March of the Three Musketeers" and the three Musketeers themselves, we will try to give you a picture of the carefree life of the Musketeers.

[*Simple drill worked out to the music. Marching forward, clashing swords, etc.*]

[*Pages exit, music continues until curtain is closed*]

SCENE X. RAMONA
Grade Nine

MUSIC: "Ramona." Tom-toms.

CHARACTERS: YOUNG INDIAN MAIDEN and BOY, dressed in Indian clothes. Two or three Indians may be used if larger cast is preferred.

SCENE: Indian scene, showing wigwam painted on wrapping paper, is dropped from center door. Two Indians sit at either side of door.

[PAGES *enter*]

VOICE: For over a half century Helen Hunt Jackson's romantic story of Spanish and Indian life in California has been widely read and has become an American classic.

In San Diego, California, a priest told Helen Hunt Jackson the true story of an Indian couple he had married in an ancient adobe mission church. He had been their confessor and counselor during their wedded life, had laid the husband in his grave, and comforted the widow throughout years of oppression.

Mrs. Jackson made this into a book called *Ramona,* as an appeal for justice to the red man. It immediately aroused feeling on the Indian question and brought about the organization of the Indian Rights Association. She did not, however, anticipate its continued popularity as a romantic story. In the last fifty years, nearly one hundred-and-fifty printings have been issued.

[Tom-toms drum softly. Chorus hums "Ramona" as curtain closes]

SCENE XI. FLORENCE NIGHTINGALE
Grade Ten

MUSIC: Part I: "Rockabye Baby."
Part II: First part of Schubert's "Impromptu."
Part III: Second part of "Impromptu" or "Rose of No Man's Land."

LIGHTING: Bright spotlight only.

SCENERY: Part I: ENGLISH GIRL of 1820, seven years old, playing with dolls, putting them to bed, mending an arm, etc. Right center.
Part II: GIRL of seventeen, applying bandage to dog, cat standing near, LITTLE BOY standing near with outstretched hand. Left center.

116

Part III: Three or four cots with WOUNDED SOLDIERS. FLORENCE NIGHTINGALE, dressed as nurse in blue cotton dress with white apron and collar and white muslin cap tied under chin, goes from one cot to the other.

[PAGES *enter*]

VOICE: Florence Nightingale, named Florence because she was born in Florence, Italy, was of English parentage. Her love and care for the sick began when she was but a little girl playing with her dolls. A doll never knew when she was very ill and would be put to bed. Florence Nightingale was born to be a nurse and a sick doll was dearer to her than a well one.

[*Spot light shifts from right center stage to left center scene*]

From her dolls she turned to caring for dogs, cats or anyone in the village who might be ill. Step by step, unconsciously, Florence Nightingale had been training her hand and eye to follow the dictates of her heart. Now a grown woman, she began to think seriously of applying this training. She spent months in the London hospitals and then visited the hospitals in Scotland and Ireland. She was horrified at the conditions. She turned to the continent and found a different state of things. Several times in her training she became ill and was forced to take a rest.

[*Scene is shifted to center stage by throwing spotlight on center scene*]

In 1854, the first battle of the Crimean war was fought. She heard the call to the women of England and immediately wrote Mr. Hebert a letter offering her services. Her efforts to organize nurses, her work among the soldiers will long be extolled. She brought comfort and cheer, and spent untold hours at her post working under adverse circumstances and conditions. She became known as the "Angel of Crimea." After

117

the war she was outstanding in her efforts for hospital reforms and training schools for nurses. She saw her good deeds begin but did not see them reach a distant goal. Florence Nightingale "still lives and loves, her thoughts still go out in tenderness and compassion toward all who are in trouble, sorrow, need, sickness, or any other adversity."

[*Music, curtain*]

SCENE XII. ABE LINCOLN IN ILLINOIS
Grade Eleven

MUSIC: "Tramp, Tramp, Tramp," "Battle Hymn of the Republic," "John Brown's Body," etc.

SCENE: Improvised platform with boy dressed as LINCOLN at front end of platform. JUDGE DOUGLAS seated on right of platform. American flag hangs from center door. Lincoln stands with hands on coat lapels. NUMBER OF PEOPLE, in the dress of the period, are scattered at either side of platform.

[PAGES *enter*]

VOICE: [*Reads selection from Lincoln's speech in the Lincoln-Douglas debate*]
[*As voice finishes, lights fade out and spotlight is thrown on Lincoln who is standing in front of the American flag. Chorus softly sings "Battle Hymn of the Republic" until curtain closes*]

SCENE XIII. THE YEARLING
Grade Twelve

MUSIC: Woodland song.

SCENE: Have the scene painted on ordinary wrapping paper, as on the jacket of book showing house and woods. Drop this from center door of shop with only bright spotlight on center. JODY stands in front of scene with young fawn (made of cambric

118

and stuffed with paper). He is dressed like the character shown on the book jacket in light working trousers and shirt (open at the neck), and is barefooted. He stands perfectly still until voice finishes.

[PAGES *enter*]

VOICE: *The Yearling,* the Pulitzer prize novel of 1939, is a story of one year in the life of a sensitive, nature-loving boy, Jody Baxter. He lived with his father and mother in the hammock country district of Florida. During that year, which brought conflict and tragedy to the Baxter family, Jody and his tame fawn, Flag, roamed the forest, hunted, and grew apace. When Flag could no longer be restrained from ruining the Baxters' precious crop, Jody faced the stark tragedy of parting with something that had become an integral part of him. As Mrs. Rawlings writes, we are all there in the scrub; and beyond the sanctuary of boyhood and the security of the clearing, struggle and burdens, fear and weariness await us all.

[*Pages exit. Curtain and music*]

CHORUS: [*sings as curtains close*]
Good night to you,
Good night to you,
Good night, dear audience,
Good night to you.

Clipper Ships

by

Winifred E. Elliott

This play was written for a Book Week program in a California Junior High School with an enrollment of about twelve hundred. As a specific theme for Book Week the Library had chosen "Clipper Ships—Old and New Style," and many angles of this subject were developed throughout the school and especially in the Library. Sea stories and aviation books, particularly those having to do with the old tea clippers and sailing vessels and books like Grooch's *Skyway to Asia,* which enhances the romance of the modern air clipper and its pioneering spirit, were featured. A large map of the world was made by the Library Club, and on it the routes of the old tea clippers, and of the modern flying ships, were plotted, and tied up with pertinent books about foreign countries then and now.

The auditorium program was planned for a forty-minute period and sought to include as many students as possible, particularly those who were not often before the public. It was done in two parts. The first part, consisting of two scenes, was illustrative of the literature of the days of the old clippers. The second part in five scenes took the form of a trip by modern airship around the world of books, with stops in five foreign countries which might conceivably appear on such a schedule. The passengers on the flying clipper were students and faculty members of the school who were entertained by natives in each country visited.

As a step toward securing "actor" material for the second half of the play, the counsellor gave the librarian a list of all students born outside the United States and those whose parents were foreign-born. The majority of these came from Latin America, Central Europe, the Orient, and the Hawaiian Islands.

An eighth-grade English class volunteered to read books with foreign country backgrounds and dramatize outstanding scenes from them.

So the national background of the students on the counsellor's list and the dramatizations of the English students formed bases for our selection of books and countries for the second part of the program.

The first part of the production introduced three well-known stories of romantic sailing experiences: Dana's *Two Years before the Mast,* Stevenson's *Treasure Island,* and Defoe's *Robinson Crusoe.* The second part finally comprised five episodes suggestive of Moon's

123

Nadita and Lee's *Marcos* (Mexico), Tschiffely's *Tale of Two Horses* (Bolivia, South America), Seredy's *The Good Master* (Hungary), Hollister's *River Children* (China), and Eskridge's *Umi* (Hawaiian Islands). The basic idea could be used to include many other titles or different ones. All books were displayed prominently in the library where their circulation subsequently increased.

Costumes were suggested by the illustrations in the books; make-up was light because many of the participants looked their parts naturally; stage settings were simple but colorful.

The most important property was the front part of a large airliner, constructed for the enterprise by the woodworking shops. It consisted of a barrel, a handsome propeller, and a framework all covered with aluminum paint to simulate the forepart of a plane resting on the ground. This peeked out between the curtains at one corner of the stage, and, with a beautiful "stage" tree nearby, furnished a permanent setting for the second half of the program. Between scenes, a vacuum cleaner was run, to sound like the motor of the plane as it travelled from place to place; e.g., Mexico to Bolivia non-stop.

Between eighty and one hundred students were actively engaged in producing this program and many of them appeared on the stage for the first time. For instance, the entertainers in Part II, Scene II were a group of non-curricular Mexican girls who, with little rehearsal, sang most effectively a folk song to their own guitar accompaniment.

A student announcer prepared the audience for each of the two portions of the program in a brief explanation of what was coming.

Clipper Ships

PART I

Incidents from some well-known voyages made by
sailing vessel

SCENE I. At sea aboard the brig "Pilgrim."

CHARACTERS:
>FIRST MATE
>SECOND MATE
>NINE OR TEN SAILORS
>VOICE IN THE RIGGING
>CAPTAIN FAUCON
>DR. LIVESEY
>JIM HAWKINS
>BEN GUNN
>ABRAHAM GRAY
>JOHN SILVER

FIRST MATE: [*Before curtain rises he shouts*] Lay aloft!
All ha-a-ands! A—ho—oy!
[*Curtain rises to show half stage as part of the deck of
an old "Tea Clipper." The first mate is standing on
deck to give orders. The men are singing a chantey as
they reef the sails, mop the deck, polish the rail, etc.
in time to the music. Half the sailors are visible on the
stage. The others sing behind the scenes. Ropes, hogs-
heads, boxes and other gear are scattered about*]
CREW: [*singing as they work, as the curtain rises*]
"As I was a-walking down Paradise Street,
Way! Hey! Blow the man down!" etc.

125

VOICE IN THE RIGGING: [*offstage to sound as though coming from the top of a mast*] Haul out to leeward!
[*Other sailors appear on deck, adjusting their clothing as though they had just come out of the rigging. They take up their stations and go to work arranging ropes, cleaning rail, etc. One takes a telescope and sets himself to watch. The first mate discovers the second mate asleep in a corner*]

FIRST MATE: [*to sailor without disturbing second mate*] Fetch the Captain!

FIRST SAILOR: Aye, aye, Mr. Hall.
[*Captain returns with sailor, who goes back to work. Captain and first mate discuss sleeping second mate at one side near front of stage*]

FIRST MATE: Just now I found the second mate asleep, sir.

CAPTAIN: Caught fair red-handed, eh? Where is he now?
[*They walk toward place where second mate sleeps. The first mate wakes the sleeping man with his boot. Second mate, startled, scrambles to his feet rubbing his eyes, etc.*]

CAPTAIN: "You're a lazy, good-for-nothing rascal; you're neither man, boy, soger nor sailor! You don't earn your salt! Go to your stateroom!"

THIRD SAILOR: [*with telescope before eyes sings out*] Sail ho!

CAPTAIN: [*going over to sailor on watch*] What name does she carry? Give me the glass. A schooner! Name, Hispaniola. We'll soon overhaul her. A landing party in a long boat is coming this way—four men and a boy, as I make them out. Lower the rope ladder! Stand by at attention!

[*Two or three sailors go off stage "aft" to meet the party which approaches. DR. LIVESEY leads. JIM HAW-*

126

KINS *is with him.* GRAY, BEN GUNN, *and* JOHN SILVER
bring up the rear]

DR. LIVESEY: Dr. Livesey is my name; ship's doctor on
the Hispaniola out of Bristol, England, sir. Captain
Smollett sends his compliments, sir. He is recovering
from a wound and is still unable to move about. Mr.
Trelawney, the owner of the Hispaniola, stayed with
the captain.

CAPTAIN: I am Captain Faucon of the brig Pilgrim, forty-
five days out of Boston, at your service. [*They shake
hands*]

DR. LIVESEY: We are on the return voyage after a success-
ful treasure hunt. We have experienced much hardship
and many adventures and have lost most of our crew.
Seeing your brig flying the American flag instead of the
Jolly Roger seemed almost an answer to prayer. We
are so short-handed that we are in a desperate state and
came aboard in the hope that you might spare us a few
good seamen till we can reach some port.

CAPTAIN FAUCON: That I cannot do, for we have a long,
hard voyage ahead. But we are near Pernambuco in
Spanish America. I suggest you sail in there where you
can surely take on men and supplies. What, may I ask,
befell your crew?

DR. LIVESEY: Some died of fever, some of wounds, and
three we left marooned perforce. It is a long story,
better told by Mr. Stevenson in *Treasure Island.* Jim
Hawkins here will never forget this voyage. Eh, Jim?

JIM HAWKINS: That I never will, sir.

CAPTAIN FAUCON: Tell us about it, Jim Hawkins.

JIM: When Mother ran the Admiral Benbow, an English
inn, sir, a man called Captain came to stay with us. He
took sick and died, and in his sea chest we found a bag
of money and a map of Treasure Island. We've had
adventure after adventure, but, to make a long story

127

short, we found the island and the treasure and are on our way home with it aboard.

CAPTAIN FAUCON: It's no wonder you're in a hurry to reach home.

DR. LIVESEY: Well, good day, sir, and may fair winds speed you on your way.

CAPTAIN FAUCON: Good day and good luck. [*Treasure Island party leaves stage as they came*] Go below the watch!

[*Half the crew of the "Pilgrim" go off stage. Another sailor takes up his post at look-out. Others work. Curtain falls*]

SCENE II. At sea aboard the brig "Pilgrim."

CHARACTERS:
  FIRST SAILOR
  SECOND SAILOR
  THIRD SAILOR
  FOURTH SAILOR
  FIFTH SAILOR
  CAPTAIN
  FIRST MATE
  ROBINSON CRUSOE
  FRIDAY (part taken by a lively colored boy)

[*Curtain rises to show watch washing down the decks*]

FIRST SAILOR: Such a watch as we have had! I shall be right glad to see breakfast.

SECOND SAILOR: Aye, after a night like last night, being becalmed is not so bad!

THIRD SAILOR: What might our bearings be?

FIRST SAILOR: About 12 degrees 40 minutes latitude and about 50 degrees longitude, so the helmsman said.

THIRD SAILOR: A nice warm spot to be stuck in! And us so near home!

[*Bell (gong) offstage sounds seven bells (7:30 a.m.)*]

128

SECOND SAILOR: Me for the salt beef and biscuits!
[*All disappear in great haste for breakfast. After the
deck is deserted,* TWO STRANGE FIGURES *dressed in skins
appear as if from over the ship's side*]

ROBINSON CRUSOE: [*examining the ship and its belongings*]
A fine ship, Friday, a fine ship!

FRIDAY: Is it white man's ship, Master?

ROBINSON: I know not. But with all sails set it looks like
a ghost ship. And quite deserted.

FOURTH SAILOR: [*running onto deck, stops short at sight
of Crusoe and Friday. Turns to fifth sailor just behind
him*] Go fetch the Captain and the Mate! We have
visitors!
[*Fifth sailor disappears, to return with* CAPTAIN FAU-
CON *and* FIRST MATE *and* OTHER SAILORS]

CAPTAIN: [*to crew*] Stand by to guard! Let them not
escape! [*to Crusoe and Friday*] How came you here
and what are your names?

ROBINSON: I am one Robinson Crusoe, for seven-and-
twenty years marooned on yonder island. And this is
my man Friday whom I rescued from cannibals and
who serves me well.

CAPTAIN: How came you aboard us?

ROBINSON: Cruising about the island to try a new canoe
we had just builded, I spied this ship through my per-
spective glass, and how she moved not though all sails
were set. So we rowed hence and boarded her. For she
is not the first ship to be abandoned in these waters.
How came you here, Captain, and whence are you
going?

CAPTAIN: We were blown off our course by last night's
storm and are now becalmed. We go toward Boston
and are on the return voyage around Cape Horn.

ROBINSON: Aye, a fine voyage.

129

FIRST MATE: Can we be of service to you, Robinson Crusoe? Your name sounds very familiar. Ah, yes! One of our sailors who reads much has mentioned a book which tells all about you.

ROBINSON: Aye, and in that same book it tells how I return to England—not to America. And so now we must go back to the island to arrange all things just as the book describes them. Thank you kindly for your offer of assistance. We are comfortable and happy and will await events in their order. Come, Friday. Bid our friends farewell.

FRIDAY: [*bowing to Captain, mate and sailors in turn*] Me go, white mans. Come some more—see our island.

ROBINSON: God Speed and pleasant weather to you all. [*Shakes hands with Captain and mate*]

CAPTAIN: Farewell, and good luck, Robinson Crusoe and Friday! May we meet again when good books get together!

[*Curtain falls as Robinson and Friday disappear over the rail and others stand watching them off*]

PART II

Clipper Ships—New Style

How a group of our own fellow-students made a trip
around the World of Books in a flying Clipper Ship.
There are five scenes laid in five places where they
stopped: Mexico, Bolivia, Hungary, China, the Hawaiian Islands. They are off! Hear their motor hum?

Scene I. Mexico. Airport at Oaxaca.

Characters:

Judy ⎤
Don ⎥   Students on Clipper as passengers
Paul ⎥
Mary ⎦
Nadita
Tita
Marcos
Juan
Chico
Pedro
Poco (little dog)
Mr. Murray (Faculty member who recently had visited Mexico)
Other Mexicans form crowd
(All the Mexican parts in this scene were played by native-born
Mexican children)

Judy: [*entering from plane and seeing (toy) dog in stage
center*] Oh! Look at this darling little dog! I wonder
whom he belongs to.

Don: Here comes a little girl now. Let's ask her.

Judy: I wonder if she speaks our language.

[Nadita *enters with* Pedro, Chico, Juan, Marcos *and*
Tita *following*]

131

NADITA: [*walking up to them and taking the dog from Judy*] Thank you so much for catching my Poco. He is a bad boy today. He ran away.

DON: Is he your dog? Where did you get him?

NADITA: Yes, he is my dog. I found him at the fountain place—[*slight pause*] Do you read books?

JUDY: Yes, we read books. Why?

NADITA: Have you ever read books by Grace Moon?

JUDY: Yes! She wrote *Indian Legends in Rhyme, Lost Indian Magic,* and lots more, too.

NADITA: She once wrote a book for me. Have you not read *Nadita*?

JUDY: Of course, I have. I remember you had an adventure with thieves and you got lost in a tunnel. Of course I read it. It was very exciting. Did those things really happen?

NADITA: [*nodding her head*] Yes, really. [*turning to other children standing near*] Here are some of my friends: Pedro, Chico, Juan, Marcos, and Tita.

JUDY: Why, I remember them. [*to Tita*] But I had forgotten your name. Won't you tell me again, please?

TITA: My full name is Titania Castilla Moreno de la Piedra, but my friends call me Tita for short. I am in a book by Mrs. Moon also.

JUDY: Oh, yes, Tita. That is a *good* book!

[MR. MURRAY *enters from plane and walks over to Marcos*]

MR. MURRAY: My name is Wallace Murray. I plan to stay here for a few days. Could you tell me where I could spend the night?

MARCOS: [*thinking*] Well, I don't know where you can get a room, but I have a little hut down the road a ways. I guess you can stay with me—if you care to.

MR. MURRAY: That will be fine! Thank you very much. Tell me, have you lived here always?

MARCOS: No, I haven't. You see, about two years ago, I left my native village to come here to the big city to Oaxaca to earn enough centavos to buy my father a pair of oxen.

MR. MURRAY: Won't you tell me about your journey? I'm sure it would be very interesting.

MARCOS: Very well, I will. I left home very early one morning with a net full of apples and my rain cape. After I had walked a long way and had traded some apples for some tortillas, I came to a bridge made of vines across a deep cañon. At first I was afraid to cross because the bridge was so high and swayed in the breeze.

MR. MURRAY: I should certainly be afraid to cross a high bridge just made of vines. It must have been pretty narrow too.

MARCOS: Yes, it was. But I finally had enough courage to cross. Then one day I came to a village where I sold the rest of my apples for fifteen centavos. With this money I went to a restaurant and ate. When it came time to pay, it cost me all of my fifteen centavos because I sat down to eat. If I had eaten standing, I should only have had to pay ten centavos.

MR. MURRAY: By the way, what is your name?

MARCOS: Marcos, Señor.

MR. MURRAY: Your story is very interesting, Marcos. No wonder we have a book in our school library about you and your adventures.

DON: [*looking at his watch*] It's almost time for the plane to leave. Good-bye, Mr. Murray. Have a good time!

MR. MURRAY: Good-bye! Have a good trip around the World of Books!

[*All call "Good-bye" and wave, as the American children go back to the plane and the curtain falls*]

133

SCENE II. BOLIVIA, SOUTH AMERICA. Airport.

CHARACTERS:
  PILOT
  CO-PILOT
  WAITER
  BOB, a student
  AUGUST
  GROUP OF NATIVES (singers and entertainers)
  SCHOOL CHILDREN PASSENGERS ON CLIPPER
  (Tables are set at the airport and a young man is drinking or
eating at one. Enter TWO AIRPLANE PILOTS who have been inspecting
the Clipper just landed from America)

PILOT: The plane looks all right, Jim.

CO-PILOT: Yes, and am I glad! That was a tough stretch
  coming over the Andes.

PILOT: I'm always glad to get to La Paz safely. The
  weather is always bad coming over, but today we were
  flying blind most of the way.

CO-PILOT: Our passengers didn't know the difference and
  that helps a lot!

PILOT: Here they come now, out to stretch their legs.
  Hello, kids, here you are in Bolivia on top of the Andes.
  Don't try to run around too much in this altitude.
  [*A group of* SCHOOL CHILDREN *enters from direction of
  plane. All present sit at tables or stand around.* WAITER
  comes out to take orders. A group of NATIVES *comes
  out to sing a Spanish song. After music all go off stage
  except two boys,* BOB *and* AUGUST, *who have been sitting
  at front table alone*]

BOB: Mind if I sit here with you?

AUGUST: No, my friend. [*He calls waiter for Bob*]

BOB: [*to waiter*] Root beer float, please.

  [*Waiter shrugs and shakes his head*]

BOB: Hot chocolate, then?

WAITER: Si, señor. [*Goes off and returns presently with
  cup and saucer*]

BOB: [*to August*] My name is Bob Hanley, what's yours?

134

AUGUST: My name is August Tschiffely.

BOB: Have you travelled far?

AUGUST: My two ponies, Mancho and Gato, and I have travelled from Patagonia.

BOB: I've travelled all the way from North America by plane to see what your country is like.

AUGUST: Mancho and Gato and I are going to walk all the way to Washington, D.C. and we hope to find out all about North America. You fly in a big bird over jungles. We walk through jungles, over mountains, through deserts and quicksand.

BOB: I must admit you have a tough time before you. How thrilling it all must be! I'd like to meet Mancho and Gato. Where are they now?

AUGUST: Come along! They are just down the street. It will take only a moment.

[*They walk off arm in arm. Curtain falls*]

SCENE III. HUNGARY. An airport. A sign reads "Budapest—4 kilometers."

CHARACTERS:
GROUND CREW FOR PLANE
MARTON NAGY, the Good Master
KATE
JANCSI
MOTHER
UNCLE SANDOR, Kate's father
(The Good Master, Kate, Jancsi, and Mother are waiting on a bench center stage. Ground crew is seen beginning work on motor of plane. Uncle Sandor steps off plane. Kate hides behind the bench)

GOOD MASTER: Here he comes now! Welcome home, Brother Sandor!

[*Enter* SANDOR]

SANDOR: Hello, everybody! Where's Kate?

135

JANCSI: [dragging Kate out] Here she is!

SANDOR: You can't fool me! That's not the girl I sent up here last summer!

KATE: Ha! Ha! He doesn't know me! I'm Kate all right, your very own spoiled and naughty daughter. [She curtsies and Sandor puts his arm around her]

SANDOR: Here Jancsi, is a gift I brought for you. Here's something for Mother. And one for Kate. And the last one is for the Good Master.

JANCSI: Thanks. O! Look! It's a riding whip! What is yours, Kate?

KATE: Mine also is a riding whip.

SANDOR: By the way, can Kate ride?

JANCSI: Can Kate ride? I wish you had been here when the horses for the fair stampeded. We both were caught in the midst of a stream of running animals. Kate led more than half the herd to the corral gate and got them in ahead of the regular herders.

SANDOR: Whew! I'll say she can ride! Good work, Kate!

KATE: Well, I had to do something. If it hadn't been for Jancsi, I shouldn't be here now.

MOTHER: Well, thank the good Lord you are both here now! It is time to go home. The good dinner will be all spoiled.

[All go off away from the plane and toward Budapest]

[CURTAIN]

SCENE IV. CHINA. An open field near Fuchow in China.

CHARACTERS:
    BING-HU ⎫
    ME-HWA ⎬ Chinese children in native dress
    DEA-DEA ⎭
    STEWARDESS OF AIRPLANE
    GROUP OF ROOSEVELT STUDENT PASSENGERS
    (Chinese children are watching the Clipper which has just made a forced landing near Fuchow in China)

136

STEWARDESS: Come now, boys and girls, it will take the crew some time to repair the plane. We can explore while we wait.

BING-HU: [*anxiously*] Little boat? Wish little boat?

STEWARDESS: Here are three nice Chinese children to greet us. How do you do? What are your names?

BING-HU: This is little sister Me-Hwa, and this is baby brother Dea-Dea. I am Bing-Hu, big brother.

FIRST AMERICAN BOY: What city are we near, Bing-Hu?

BING-HU: You are quite near the great city of Fuchow.

FIRST AMERICAN GIRL: And how could we get to Fuchow?

ME-HWA: We have a little sampan and could take you down the river. But it is several miles to the city.

STEWARDESS: Our plane just made a forced landing, and we may have to stay some time. Is there a place near by where we can stop?

ME-HWA: The Good-to-Love Lady and her First Born have a large house. I am sure you would all be welcome there.

SECOND AMERICAN GIRL: Can you take us to this place?

ME-HWA: Oh, yes, the Good-to-Love Lady is very nice. She asked us to stay with her when our Big People were taken away by the plague.

THIRD AMERICAN GIRL: What fun to stay in a real Chinese home! Could we really do that?

STEWARDESS: Perhaps it can be arranged. Shall we go and see?

BING-HU: This way, please. [*Leads everyone off stage left*]

[CURTAIN]

137

SCENE V. HAWAII. An airport on the Island of Hawaii.

CHARACTERS:

LILOA, King of Hawaii
UMI, Prince of Hawaii
HAKAU, Prince of Hawaii
MONA
KIM
OTHER HAWAIIANS
LEILANI—Narrator
SIX ROOSEVELT STUDENTS

[*As curtain rises, Students come from plane led by Leilani and other Hawaiian girls as beating drums are heard in the distance. A procession of Hawaiian men and boys dressed in feathered capes, etc. cross the back of the stage slowly and stop in tableau stage center as drums slowly fade out*]

FIRST GIRL STUDENT: How exciting! Whatever is happening?

LEILANI: Umi has just been made a prince.

FIRST BOY STUDENT: And who is Umi?

LEILANI: Liloa, King of Hawaii, has found his son at last and has had him crowned as prince in a great ceremony. They are now on their way to a feast at the palace.

SECOND BOY STUDENT: Which one is Umi?

LEILANI: The boy on this side in the long feather cloak and helmet. These things denote royalty.

SECOND GIRL STUDENT: Everyone looks very happy.

LEILANI: Yes, everyone loves Umi. All his life he has lived with his foster parents in the country, but he has been a great hero to his friends. By his bravery in going down the slide he learned that Liloa was his father and Hakau his brother. Now he will help to rule Hawaii.

138

THIRD BOY STUDENT: And what will they have to eat at the feast?

LEILANI: Oh, roast pig, of course, and fish, and poi, our national food, and Hawaiian fruits of all sorts. The women have been preparing the food for hours.

THIRD GIRL STUDENT: How romantic it all sounds when you tell it, Leilani. I hate to leave Hawaii.

STEWARDESS: But we must get back to California and the Roosevelt school. Think how long we have been away!

LEILANI: If you must go, let's all sing Aloha Oe together. Then you will be sure to return some day.

[Leilani and girls place leis around students' necks as everybody on stage including the procession sings. Curtain falls]

[Curtain rises once more to show everyone who has taken part grouped on stage safely at home again, and the audience joins the players in singing the school song]

139

Book Friends
by
Alice Pollok

No royalty charged for production

This play has been successfully produced in a Junior High School several times. It may be produced by a library club, an English class, or by any other group for book week or to create an interest in reading. It may also be given as a graduation play to show the use of the library. Playing time: 30-35 minutes.

CHARACTERS:

BOB
JEAN
SYLVIA } Members of the Library Club
DORIS
DAVID, a boy who pays a fine
MARY, a girl who pays a fine
JOSEPHINE, a girl who comes in to borrow a book
SAM and ARTHUR, boys who come in with an overdue night book
JOHN, a boy who borrows a book
ELLEN, Sylvia's little cousin, about to enter Junior High School

ALICE
WHITE RABBIT
TOM SAWYER
HUCKLEBERRY FINN } Fiction
ROBIN HOOD
LITTLE JOHN
WILL SCARLET
THREE MERRY MAIDS

ISABELLA, QUEEN OF SPAIN
SIR WALTER RALEIGH
MARTHA WASHINGTON } History
GEORGE WASHINGTON
TWO COLONIAL GENTLEMEN
TWO COLONIAL LADIES

CHEF
SEWING MAGAZINE GIRL } Cooking, Sewing and Poetry
BOY WHO READS POEM

143

GRETEL, German girl ⎫
OLGA and NINA, Russian girls ⎬ Geography
HEIDI, Swiss ⎭

All characters enter and leave through the double doors at the back of center stage.

SETTING: The stage is set to represent a library with bookshelves filled with books, along the wall, a desk at the left stage and a small mending table at the right stage. There is a wagon with books on it near rear right wall. Bob takes books from here and places them on the shelf.

PROPS: Huckleberry Finn carries an old fur which represents a dead cat.

COSTUMES: The school children are dressed in typical school clothes. The book characters may be costumed according to pictures of them in well illustrated books.

LIGHTING: While the library activities are going on there is an amber light. When Doris turns out the light for the book characters to come on there is a blue light. A spot light is used when the characters come on.

MUSIC: The tunes for "Good Morrow, Gossip Joan" and for "The Keeper" can be found in *A Book of Songs for Unison and Part Singing for Grades IV-V-VI.* (Concord Series No. 14. Teachers' Edition) E. C. Schirmer Music Company, 221 Columbia Avenue, Boston, Mass.

The numbers of books may be changed to fit the circulation of any school library.

TIME: 3:45
Children in the Library are finishing up for the day.
    BOB is slipping books.
    JEAN is mending books at a table.
    SYLVIA is sorting books on a truck preparing to shelve them.
    DORIS has the librarian's place and is at desk answering questions, stamping books, etc.
Six or eight children come in to get or return books.

144

Book Friends

DAVID: May I see Miss Idleman? I have a fine.

DORIS: Miss Idleman is at a teacher's meeting but I will take care of your fine. I belong to the Library Club and am taking Miss Idleman's place.
[*David pays and leaves. Bob laughs*]

SYLVIA: What are you laughing at, Bob? Did you read something funny?

BOB: No, but I found something funny. Just look at this— a bathing cap in a book! It's a wonder to me that some of these kids don't turn in an overcoat or a pair of socks.

DORIS: Oh, dear! I wish we could teach the children to be more thoughtful of their books. It is so hard on a book to put things in it. It breaks the binding in no time.

BOB: Well, even if they didn't care about the book, you'd think they'd think more of their own property. Look, here are five pencils, three rulers, an eraser, no end of papers and a bathing cap. Say, if you'll let me help you for the rest of the term I can set up in business. [*Holds up articles as he speaks*]

[*MARY enters and goes to the desk*]

DORIS: I certainly wish we could do something about it.

BOB: Oh, I think things are getting better. I don't get half as many odds and ends since we had that library home-room meeting. The worst thing I ever found was a yo-yo, but every rainy day I look for an umbrella.

145

SYLVIA: Try and find out who leaves the things, Bob. Perhaps it would do some good to talk to the owners.

BOB: I'll make a list.

MARY: Shall I have to pay a fine? My book was due yesterday but my mother told me to come home early, so I forgot to return my book.

DORIS: Yes, indeed, Mary, that will be two cents.

[JOSEPHINE *enters*]

MARY: But my Mother told me to hurry home.

DORIS: I know, but it only takes a minute or two to check in a book.

MARY: Here it is then.

[*Mary goes out*]

JOSEPHINE: May I have the book I was reading last Wednesday when my class was here?

[JOHN *enters*]

DORIS: What was the name of the book?

JOSEPHINE: I don't know, but it was about a girl.

DORIS: Do you know her name?

JOSEPHINE: No, but I know it was a red book, and somebody Alcott wrote it.

DORIS: I'm sorry, but you see, we have hundreds of red books. I guess I can't help you unless you remember the name, or maybe you could find it in the card catalog by looking under Louisa May Alcott.

JOHN: Will you give me a book about General Custard?

DORIS: You mean General Custer, don't you, John? C-u-s-t-e-r.

JOHN: I guess so. Was he the Indian fighter? I'm crazy about Indian fights.

DORIS: Look for General Custer under biography books. Sylvia, show John how to use the files, will you please?

[*Sylvia directs John to the file*]

[SAM *and* ARTHUR *enter*]

146

SAM: [*patently making excuses*] Here's the one-day book I forgot to leave at the desk before eight-thirty this morning. You see, I was nearly late for class. Our baby is teething and I had to go to the drug store for toothache wax. That doesn't call for a fine now, does it?

DORIS: Five cents, please.

SAM: Oh, all right then. [*Searches for the money first in one pocket, then in another*] I had it a minute ago. [*Finds it and hands it to Doris*] Oh, here it is.

ARTHUR: [*making fun of Sam*] I told you it wouldn't work. Even if you told her your baby brother was blown up by a stick of dynamite, that nickel would have to be cashed in.

[*Sam and Arthur leave, Arthur still making fun of Sam*]

BOB: Whew! I'm through. 421 [1] books in one day! I call that a lot.

SYLVIA: That is a lot of books for one day, and that doesn't count half the children that have been in I'll bet.

DORIS: No, it doesn't. We had exactly 839 [1] children in and out of this library today. Of course, this is a big day, but then we often have big days.

JEAN: No wonder we have to mend so many books. They get so much use.

DORIS: And we don't have enough. I heard Miss Idleman say we only had about 2,000 [1] books to begin with, and we only have about 2,800 [1] now. You'd think we could do better than that in four [1] years.

JEAN: Well, we borrow a lot from the school department every week. That helps out, too.

[*3:45 bell rings*]

BOB: Oh! There's the bell. I'll have to hurry to get to the "Y" in time for swimming.

[1] Figures can be changed to suit.

147

JEAN: Me, too, I have to do some shopping.

[*Exit Jean and Bob followed by John and Josephine who get their books stamped and leave*]

SYLVIA: Well, I'm staying for a while. My little cousin is coming up this evening. She'll be coming here next semester and she doesn't know a soul, so I want to show her the library and other parts of the building tonight. Then it won't be so strange to her when she starts here next week.

DORIS: I'll wait and walk home with you. Do you think she'll be long?

SYLVIA: She should be here any minute now.

[*Bob comes back to the door with Ellen, Sylvia's cousin*]

BOB: Here's your cousin, Sylvia.

[ELLEN *enters, Bob leaves*]

SYLVIA: Hello, Ellen!

ELLEN: Hello, Sylvia!

SYLVIA: Doris, this is my little cousin, Ellen Williams; I should like you to know each other. Ellen, this is Doris King.

DORIS: How do you do, Ellen.

ELLEN: How do you do, are you in 9A, too?

DORIS: Yes. Sylvia tells me that you would like to visit our library. How do you like it?

ELLEN: It's lovely, so cheerful and gay! [*walking around inspecting the library*]

SYLVIA: It is a lovely room, Ellen, but it's the friends I've made here I want you to meet.

ELLEN: Friends? I don't see any one here except Doris.

SYLVIA: That's because you aren't observant. There are hundreds of friends here just waiting to be introduced.

ELLEN: You're fooling me!

SYLVIA: No, I'm not. I'll introduce my fiction friends first. Just turn out the lights. It's easier that way.

[*Doris turns out the lights, leaving the stage in blue*

148

twilight. The girls are grouped near the desk at one side]

ELLEN: What's fiction?

SYLVIA: Make believe stories. My favorite is Alice in Wonderland. Here, open this book and you shall see Alice. [*Hands book to Ellen who opens it. Sylvia claps her hands and calls*] "Alice! Alice!"

[*Out runs* ALICE, *followed by the* WHITE RABBIT]

ALICE: Thanks, Sylvia, for getting me out of that stuffy old book. Oh, dear! I've been trying and trying to teach this stupid rabbit to dance, but all he can do is flap one foot. Here Rabbit, try this [*doing a dance step*]

RABBIT: [*wrong step*] Like this?

ALICE: [*showing him how*] Like this.

RABBIT: [*wrong step*] Like this?

ALICE: [*showing him again*] Like this.

RABBIT: [*wrong*] Like this?

ALICE: [*Shows him again*] Here, like this.

RABBIT: Here, I'll show you. I don't believe you know how to do it, anyhow.

[*Alice and the Rabbit do a short eccentric dance and dance off stage*]

ELLEN: How delightful. What a queer pair of friends.

SYLVIA: Well, here are another queer pair.

[*Enter* HUCKLEBERRY FINN *with dead cat followed by* TOM SAWYER]

TOM: Gee! Huck! Let me see that old cat again. [*Inspects cat*] Do you think it will really do the job?

HUCK: Do the job? Of course it will do the job. Didn't I tell you old Mother Hopkins told me so?

TOM: [*handing cat back to Huck*] Doesn't smell very good. Maybe it's too far gone to take off your warts.

HUCK: A cat's never too far gone to take off warts. Why the farther it's gone the better it takes 'em off.

149

TOM: Can't you use it any place but a cemetery? That's a funny place to go at night.

HUCK: If you have to do a thing you have to do it right, don't you? And if it's a cemetery it's a cemetery, isn't it? Are you goin' or ain't you?

TOM: Course I'm goin'! What you gettin' sore at? Can't a feller ask a question?

HUCK: Sure, but it's about midnight. We've got to hurry. What's the use of goin' if we get there too late.

TOM: [*in a hushed tone*] Midnight! Gee, Huck. What if there are ghosts?

[*Tom and Huck go off talking*]

ELLEN: What funny boys they are. Did they ever go to the grave-yard?

DORIS: Yes, they did, but if you want to know more you must read about them in Mark Twain's books.

ELLEN: Oh my! I'm all excited! Let me meet somebody else.

DORIS: Then let it be Robin Hood. [*Claps hands*]

[*Enter* ROBIN HOOD, LITTLE JOHN, *and* WILL SCARLET, *followed by* THREE MERRY MAIDS. *They enter singing an old English ballad "The Keeper." When they have finished, they do an old English dance. The company passes off the stage*]

ELLEN: How lovely! I don't think I want to meet any but fiction friends.

DORIS: Oh, that wouldn't be fair to yourself, Ellen. You'd miss all the interesting characters of History, the lovely Poetry and the people of Geography and Science.

ELLEN: I don't think they are so interesting.

DORIS: Perhaps that is because you have only met them in a textbook. Textbooks are all right, but it's the outside reading that makes a subject seem real.

SYLVIA: Whom would you like to meet first, Ellen?

ELLEN: Oh! The people from History, I guess.

SYLVIA: History it shall be then.

[*A* PAGE *steps forward and recites while three tableaux follow*]

FIRST TABLEAUX

PAGE:

From out the pages of the past,
There steps a man you know full well.
Columbus kneels and thus receives
The jewels of lovely Isabel.

[COLUMBUS *enters slowly and dejectedly. He stands folding and unfolding his hands.* ISABELLA *enters and calls Columbus by name*]

ISABELLA: Columbus!

COLUMBUS: [*Drops to one knee*] My Lady.

ISABELLA: I had you sent here that I might, with my own hands, give you my jewels. They will pay for ships that you may go to the Indies.

[*Columbus, kneeling, receives the box of jewels, then kisses the hem of Isabella's dress*]

ISABELLA: Now come with me. There are many plans to make. [*Exit Isabella followed by Columbus*]

ELLEN: How real they seemed. Of course, I've met them before, but they never seemed so—so flesh and blood.

SECOND TABLEAUX

PAGE:

The years roll back and once again,
A gallant gentleman is seen,
Sir Walter Raleigh doffs his coat,
For fair Elizabeth, the Queen.

[SIR WALTER RALEIGH *comes in with a jaunty gait. He struts back and forth.* QUEEN ELIZABETH *enters soon after and stops near Raleigh as though she has*

151

come to a pool. *Raleigh steps toward her, bows, and with a flourish lays his cloak for the Queen to step upon. Elizabeth walks across it and speaks*]

ELIZABETH: Well done my noble sir. I go now to knight you in my royal court. I will see that the world soon hears of your chivalrous deed.

[*Raleigh bows low. Exit Elizabeth. Raleigh picks up his cloak and follows Elizabeth*]

ELLEN: So that's how he did it! It was a gallant thing to do, but such a shame to spoil his beautiful new coat.

THIRD TABLEAUX

PAGE:

> George Washington, in lighter moods,
> Would often lead a minuet
> Mount Vernon's spacious halls resound,
> With echos of the music yet.

[MARTHA *and* GEORGE *step out of the picture and do a minuet with* TWO OTHER COUPLES]

ELLEN: Oh, dear! I wish I'd lived in those days. When I come up here I'll read nothing but fiction and history.

SYLVIA: Oh, you will? What about your sewing classes and cooking classes?

ELLEN: What has the library to do with the sewing and cooking?

DORIS: Plenty. Look here.

[*Boy dressed as* CHEF *steps out, followed by* SEWING MAGAZINE GIRL *stylishly dressed. Boy carries cook book. Girl carries magazine*]

CHEF:

> If it's etiquette you're looking for
> In dressing up your table
> You'll find it in the Cook book

152

Under just the proper label.
But if, perchance, a cake you'd bake
To just the right degree
You'll find the full instructions
With your favorite recipe.

SEWING MAGAZINE GIRL:
The magazines are such a boon
In keeping up to date.
I really don't know what I'd do
Without a fashion plate.
Now *Vogue* is such a comfort
When your wardrobe's in distress
You can always pick a pattern
And make yourself a dress.

[Exit Chef and Sewing Magazine Girl]

ELLEN: She's right. The magazines certainly do keep a person up to date. This is getting better and better. What other kinds of books are here?

DORIS: Many, but for pure enjoyment there is nothing to take the place of poetry.

SYLVIA: Don't you love that beautiful poem "The Creation" [2] by J. W. Johnson?

ELLEN: Who was he?

DORIS: You mean who is he? He is one of the outstanding Negro poets of America. He lives in New York,[3] but he often reads his poetry in other cities.

ELLEN: I should like to hear that poem, "The Creation."

SYLVIA: You shall.

[Boy steps forward and recites "The Creation"]

[2] Any other modern poem and poet may be used here. A Negro child should read "The Creation" if it is possible.

[3] If another poet is used the dialogue should be altered accordingly.

ELLEN: How lovely. I never knew poetry could be so grand.

DORIS: It's getting so late, Sylvia, don't you think we'd better go?

ELLEN: Not yet, please.

SYLVIA: Well, we'll introduce you to some friends from Geography and then we must go.

DORIS: Here is Gretel from Germany. She may sing if you are quiet.

[GERMAN GIRL *sings in native language*]

ELLEN: She sings beautifully, but I can't understand her.

DORIS: Perhaps you will some day, if you study her language.

SYLVIA: Here is Olga from Russia. She and her sister Nina will dance.

[*Enter* OLGA *and* NINA *and perform a Russian dance*]

DORIS: Come now. Miss Idleman told us to close up at 4:30, if she wasn't back from the meeting.

ELLEN: But there are so many more interesting people here. Just one more, please.

DORIS: Just one more then. Who shall it be?

SYLVIA: I know. Heidi! She's just the one. She is a fiction character but there are many real Heidies in Switzerland.

DORIS: Heidi! Heidi! Won't you come and sing for us?

[HEIDI *enters*]

HEIDI: Did some one call me? My name is Heidi and I live high in the mountains of Switzerland. Would you like to hear about it?

DORIS, SYLVIA AND ELLEN: We'd love to.

[*Heidi sings "My Echo", with echo answering back stage*]

154

My Echo

1. In my moun - tain home I am quite con - tent While in tend - ing my goats My

days are spent. If I ev - er get lone - ly All I have to do Is call to my Ech-o Yoo-

hoo (Yoo-hoo) Yoo-hoo (Yoo-hoo) Yoo- hoo (Yoo-hoo) - Yoo-hoo (Yoo-hoo) Yoo-hoo (Yoo-hoo) If I

Echo. Echo Echo Echo

ev - er get lonely all I have to do Is (call to my Echo Yoo-hoo (Yoo-hoo)

[Echo

    2. When the days are bright
        And the skies are blue
        I watch my goats
        The whole day through
        If I ever get lonely
        All I have to do
        Is call to my echo Yoo-hoo, Yoo-hoo.
        Yoo-hoo, Yoo-hoo, Yoo-hoo, Yoo-hoo
        Yoo-hoo, Yoo-hoo, Yoo-hoo, Yoo-hoo
        If I ever get lonely
        All I have to do
        Is call to my echo, Yoo-hoo, Yoo-hoo

HEIDI: Good-by. Come and visit me some day. [*Runs off*]

SYLVIA: Now we must go. It is getting late.

ELLEN: Oh, I hate to go. I hate to leave all these people.

SYLVIA: You must meet them some other time. Orders are orders. You can make a lot of friends in the three years you will be here.

ELLEN: But how?

SYLVIA: Just take a book from the shelf.

[*All book characters come on singing, "Just take a Book from the Shelf" to the tune of "Good Morrow, Gossip Joan" (See opposite page)*]

SECOND STANZA:

    2. If you would like to roam,
        We must arrange a meeting
        We'll sail across the foam, the foam,
        We'll sail across the foam, the foam,
        So don't delay our meeting
        Come take us home.

[CURTAIN]

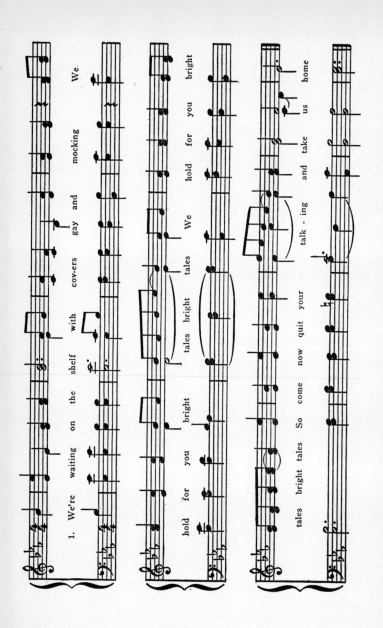

In the School Library

by

Elsie Padgett

DIRECTIONS:

The stage is arranged as a school library, with bookshelves and books, card catalog, vertical file, dictionary on stand, attractive bulletin board and periodical rack. There should be three entrances, if possible, in order that the Enemies may enter from different directions.

The Spirit of the Library should be an older, taller girl in blue evening dress. The Catalog Cards wear large pieces of cardboard marked properly to represent catalog cards. The Dewey Classification Numbers wear smaller pieces of cardboard with the numbers on them. The Spirit of the Dictionary and Spirit of the Encyclopedia wear bright dresses and cardboard crowns with the words *Dictionary* and *Encyclopedia* on them. These two girls should be hidden or in shadow until their turn comes to speak. The Enemies wear black masks. The Book should be a very small boy since he has to be lifted by the Turners-Down. A large piece of black cardboard for a cover, with white papers for pages, is made to resemble a book, and he wears this hung from his neck by a cord and steadied by his hands at the sides. The book should cover him in front from neck to knee. The pages should carry printing and pictures on them. The Book wears a golden crown.

Lighting should be subdued.

In the School Library

CHARACTERS:

SPIRIT OF LIBRARY — a tall girl

RUTH } two Junior High School girls
JOAN }

000-099 }
100-199 }
200-299 }
300-399 }
400-499 }
500-599 } ten girls
600-699 }
700-799 }
800-899 }
900-999 }

AUTHOR CARD }
TITLE CARD } three girls
SUBJECT CARD }

SPIRIT OF DICTIONARY

SPIRIT OF ENCYCLOPEDIA

ENEMIES:

DIRTY HANDS }
WATER }
INK }
HEAT }
KNIVES } eight boys and a girl
LIPSTICK }
THUMBING }
SCISSORS }
TURNERS-DOWN }

THE BOOK — a small boy

[*Curtain rises. Soft music continues through speech of Spirit of Library. Enter* SPIRIT OF THE LIBRARY]

SPIRIT OF LIBRARY:

    This is the place where live the best of books—
    The wisdom of an unforgotten past,
    The charming tale, the mellow verse, the pages
      dipped
    In rich experience and beauty that shall last.
    And all for those whose eager feet shall cross
    The threshold of this room—the children who
    Shall enter here to find some worth, some joy
    In reading,—joy and worth forever new. [*Spirit
      withdraws to back of stage*]

    [*Enter* JOAN *and* RUTH *at right*]

RUTH: [*timidly*] What room is this?

JOAN: I don't know, but I'm going to find out.

RUTH: Oh let's don't! On our first day in Junior High we ought not to be prowling around and getting into things. I'm sure the teachers won't like it.

JOAN: Why it isn't even our first day in school! We only came to register and to get our books. Besides, I saw lots of visitors coming here this morning. [*They look around curiously at everything*]

JOAN: Why, look at all the books!

RUTH: And here is a dictionary, like ours in the library at home.

JOAN: Maybe that's what this is—a library.

    [*Spirit of Library comes forward*]

SPIRIT OF LIBRARY: Welcome to the school library!

JOAN: Library?

RUTH: Who are you?

SPIRIT OF LIBRARY: When you speak that magic word *library* I come, for I am the Spirit of the Library. This is the room where you will spend many happy hours.

RUTH: Shall we come here every day?

SPIRIT OF LIBRARY: Yes, every day, if you like.

JOAN: Why?

SPIRIT OF LIBRARY: Because the library has much to give you. There is knowledge for you; there is help for your work; and, best of all, there is fun here for you. Some of the finest of all companions are waiting for you in their places on the shelves. Here are *Huckleberry Finn* and *Tom Sawyer* [*touching the shelves as she speaks*]; here is *Anne of Green Gables*; here are the *Little Women*; here are *Jim Davis* and *Mrs. Wiggs* and *David Copperfield* and *Master Skylark*. Here are *Understood Betsy* and *Rebecca of Sunnybrook Farm*.

RUTH: Is that what a library is for—knowledge and fun?

SPIRIT OF LIBRARY: Yes, that is what all libraries are for.

JOAN: Why do you have all these things in the library? [*Indicates furniture, etc.*]

SPIRIT OF LIBRARY: Would you really like to know? Would you like to see all my helpers—the helpers of all people who use books?

BOTH: Oh, yes!
[*Enter* NUMBERS. *Music*]

SPIRIT OF LIBRARY: These are my very good helpers—the Dewey classification numbers. The Dewey system was invented by Melvil Dewey, director of libraries for the State of New York. In libraries everywhere you will find these numbers, glad and happy to find books for you. Try them and see.

RUTH: [*to the Numbers*] Please, will you find me a book that tells about St. Augustine? I was there last week.

900: I am History. I will show you a book that tells how St. Augustine was founded in 1565 by the Spaniards.

JOAN: Which one of you will find me a book of poems? I love poems.

800: I am Literature. Here is a book of poems for you—*Golden Numbers* compiled by Kate Douglas Wiggin.

RUTH: And I want a book of pictures—I love pictures as much as Joan loves poems.

700: I am Fine Arts—I will find you a book of pictures—*Apollo* by Reinach. And here is another book you will like—*How Music Grew* by Marion Bauer.

JOAN: [*to 600*] Can *you* find me a good book?

600: Indeed I can. I am Useful Arts. I have books on medicine and engineering. Here is a book on poultry farming, and here is one on airplanes. Maybe a little girl like you would prefer a book on cooking and sewing. I have those, too.

RUTH: Where are the books about animals?

500: Here is one—*J. T. jr; the Biography of an African Monkey* by Mrs. Delia Akeley; or you can have *Wild Animals I Have Known* by Ernest Thompson Seton. I am the number which will guide you to all the sciences—chemistry, physics, botany, and many others.

JOAN: And what can you find for me, Number 400?

400: [*importantly*] I am Language. I can find you a dictionary, or a book that tells you how to write a letter. You will need me!

300: And I can give you a book that tells you all about how countries are governed and how people live.

RUTH: Fine!

200: Could you do without me? I am Religion. This beautifully illustrated book of Bible stories belongs to me. I can tell you the myths and legends of other lands—here are the stories of Greece and Rome.

RUTH: Oh, I'm going to like you! Do you have the story of the Golden Apple?

200: Yes, and the stories of the Northland.

JOAN: [*to 100*] Then who are *you?*

100: I am a big word—Philosophy. But for you I have such pleasant books as *Young Folks' Book of Ideals* by Forbush, and *The Right Thing* by Stevens.

RUTH: [*to 000*] Well, you are so little—what can be left for you to show us?

000: I am Zero, but I can show you the biggest books of all, the books of general reference, the encyclopedias. All the periodicals, too, belong to me—*Scholastic, American Girl, Newsweek*. Would you like one?

[*Ruth and Joan step back a little and sing to Numbers*]

(Tune, "*O My Darling Clementine*")

How do you do?
How do you do?
Dewey numbers,
How do you do?
We are very glad to know you,
And to learn your meaning, too.
We shall use you,
We shall use you,
You will guide us on our way,
Pointing out the books we ask for,
You will serve us every day.

SPIRIT OF LIBRARY: But suppose you want to call a Dewey helper and don't know which one to call. Shall I show you my helpers in the card catalog?

JOAN: Oh, yes.

RUTH: We want to see them.

SPIRIT OF LIBRARY: In this catalog are three kinds of cards. [*Waves wand. Enter* CARDS] This kind is called an author card.

AUTHOR CARD: On me is written first the name of the author, then the title of the book, then the date and place of publication with the name of the publisher. You may find out whether or not my book is illustrated, and how many pages it has. I can tell you whether or not the book is translated from another language.

165

TITLE CARD: I tell you first the *title* of the book, and you can find a book by me even if you have forgotten the name of the author.

SUBJECT CARD: I tell you the subject of the book. My first line is always written in red.

TOGETHER: Catalog cards are we—

AUTHOR CARD: The author is given by me—

TITLE CARD: The title I tell you, you see—

SUBJECT CARD: The subject in red will be—

TOGETHER: Catalog cards are we! [*They bow*]

SPIRIT OF LIBRARY: And in the corner of each is the classification number. Thank you, Catalog Cards. This card says—[*She reads from one of the cards—then continues*]

Sometimes in the corner of the card we find the letter R which stands for Reference. Reference books are on separate shelves and have to be used so often that they are not taken from the library. The library has other valuable material in this vertical file which you may examine for yourselves. [*They do so*] But have you seen this good old friend, the dictionary? Spirit of the Dictionary, will you tell these girls about yourself?

SPIRIT OF DICTIONARY: [*absorbed in pages of dictionary, recites in a singsong*]

> aback, abandon, abase,
> badly, bravely, bear,
> cruel, craven, case,
> dirty, dollar, dare,
> easy, earning, ear,
> follow, fatal, flat,
> glowing, giggle, gone,
> hardly, heaven, hat.

[*Looks up as if seeing the girls for the first time*] What can I do for you, little girls?

166

RUTH: Oh, tell us all about yourself!

SPIRIT OF DICTIONARY: I am full of knowledge for you! I can tell you how to spell and pronounce words, what they mean, and where they come from. I have many pictures. I can tell you all the places of the world and how to pronounce their names. I am very, very important.

JOAN: We are glad to meet you. We really had no idea you were so full of things. Can you tell me what my name means? My name is Joan.

SPIRIT OF DICTIONARY: [*turning pages rapidly*] O yes, "Joan, feminine name—a rustic lass."

JOAN: But what does *rustic* mean?

SPIRIT OF DICTIONARY: [*turning pages rapidly again*] "of or pertaining to the country; awkward, rough, unpolished."

JOAN: Oh dear, I'm not rough and unpolished, I know.

SPIRIT OF DICTIONARY: Never mind, let me introduce you to the encyclopedia.

SPIRIT OF ENCYCLOPEDIA: Yes, I am here, and full to the brim of interesting information. I can tell you how long it takes a bird to build a nest, who carried the first grains of corn to Europe, who the "Green Mountain Boys" were, where the largest bell in the world may be found, and how to make a bow and arrow.

RUTH: Do you know all that? I shall visit you often, bringing a notebook and a pencil, for I have many things to ask you.

SPIRIT OF LIBRARY: There are many other reference books in the library. You will learn to use them all—the *World Almanac, Who's Who in America,* and a dozen more. But here is the person who is most important of all. Welcome to His Majesty, the Book!

[*All step back to rear and sides of stage, bowing low*

167

as BOOK *enters. He walks grandly to stately music, bowing graciously to left and right*]

BOOK: Thank you, my loyal subjects!

[*impressively*]

> I am His Majesty, the Book.
> Precious are my pages,
> Filled with fancy, fact and fun,
> And wisdom of the ages.
> My title page will tell you all
> About my publication;
> My index alphabetical
> Will give you information
> On how to find just what you want;
> My chapter headings all
> Are in the table of contents;
> My footnotes may be small,
> But they are very helpful,
> Whenever students call.
> I am His Majesty the Book!
> Thank you, my subjects all.

JOAN: I'm afraid that we have not appreciated you, Your Majesty! I have paid not a bit of attention to your table of contents or your footnotes. Never have I looked at your title page or your index. Please forgive me!

[*Enter the* ENEMIES *from left, center, and right singing. They surround and terrify the Book*]

SONG OF THE ENEMIES
(*Tune, "When Johnny Comes Marching Home"*)

1. We are the enemies of books—beware—beware—
   We treat them badly and spoil their looks—take care—take care—
   We thumb their pages and break their backs
   And grease them well with between-meal snacks—
   We are the enemies of books—beware—
   We are the enemies of books—beware.

2. We are the enemies of books—beware—beware—
   We leave them out in forgotten nooks—take care—
      take care—
   We pounce upon them and, quick as a wink,
   We snip with shears and we blot with ink—
   We are the enemies of books—beware—
   We are the enemies of books—beware.

DIRTY HANDS: I am Dirty Hands. I spoil clean white pages. I am one of the worst enemies of books. [*Reaches over and leaves print of a dirty hand on a page of the Book*]

WATER: Water, too, is very harmful to books. Sometimes books are left out in the rain. They are never strong again, and have to be invalid books all their lives. [*Shoots water on the Book from a toy gun*]

INK: I am Ink. Careless boys and girls make books unhappy by spilling ink on their pages. [*Squirts ink from a fountain pen*]

HEAT: How about heat? When books are left on the radiator or near the stove, the binding is loosened, and the book may fall apart. [*Plays the light of an electric torch over the Book*]

KNIVES: Knives, too, are very dangerous to books. Some boys who like to whittle cut off little pieces of pages or binding. I can spoil a book very quickly. [*Cuts page*]

LIPSTICK: Boys are not the only guilty ones. I am Lipstick, and, oh, what I can do to a book. [*Smears page*]

THUMBING: I am one of the very old enemies of books. Only people who do not love books turn down their pages to mark the place. [*Turns down corner of page*] How does the Book look now?

SCISSORS: I am very unpleasant—no one is a worse enemy of books than I am! I am Scissors and sometimes I

169

cut a whole page at once, particularly if it has nice illustrations. [*Slashes at the Book*]

TURNERS-DOWN: [*in unison*] How about us? We are the terrible people who turn books down on their faces and break their backs—We break their backs and rumple their leaves—let's go! [*They pick up the Book and lay him face downward with rumpled leaves. The Book lies quietly while Ruth and Joan rush in and scatter the Enemies who take their places around the stage with backs to the audience and heads hanging in shame*]

RUTH: [*tenderly, as she and Joan gently raise the Book to his feet*] We shall never, never treat you badly!

JOAN: We shall never, never be friends with the Enemies of books!

RUTH: I know some friends of books—paste and clean fingers and scissors for mending and book markers.

JOAN: [*vigorously*] And these Enemies may as well become friends. [*The two girls turn each Enemy around, shaking each as they do so. The Enemies stand, chastened and forgiven*]

RUTH: What a lot of us there are!

JOAN: And we are all friends of books!
[*All join in the closing chorus*]

HERE'S TO A GOOD BOOK
(Tune, "*Solomon Levi*")

1. There are many pleasant things to do
   For a boy or girl in school—
   There are games to play and songs to sing,
      And happiness is the rule.
      But if you want the finest fun,
         You'll find it if you look
   For the many joys contained within
   The covers of a book!

170

CHORUS: So here's to a good book—
Tra la la la la la la—
A cheer for a good book—
Tra la la la la la la la la la la la—
If you want the finest fun,
You'll find it if you look
For the many joys contained within
The covers of a book!

2. But everyone who loves a book
Must take the greatest care
To keep its pages clean and white—
Its covers fresh and fair—
Then, if you want a faithful friend,
You'll find one if you look
Within that home of faithful friends—
The covers of a book!

CHORUS:

[CURTAIN]

The Magic Book
by
Ann Anderson

Acknowledgment is gratefully made to the publishers who have permitted excerpts from their books to be quoted or adaptations to be made: to Little Brown and Co. for *Little Women*; Charles Scribner's Sons, for *Treasure Island*; Harper & Bros. for *The Adventures of Tom Sawyer*; Doubleday, Doran & Co. Inc. for *Penrod and Sam*; John C. Winston Co. for *Alice in Wonderland*; The Macmillan Co. for *Little Black Sambo*; and Houghton, Mifflin Co. for *Rebecca of Sunnybrook Farm*.

The Magic Book

ROBERT
BERESFORD } children in school clothes
NANCY

MEG
JO
BETH } from *Little Women*
AMY
LAURIE

TOM SAWYER }
HUCK FINN } from *Tom Sawyer*

PENROD from *Penrod and Sam*

ALICE }
HATTER } from *Alice in Wonderland*

JOHN SILVER from *Treasure Island*
LITTLE BLACK SAMBO

REBECCA }
EMMA JANE } from *Rebecca of Sunnybrook Farm*

GEORGE WASHINGTON
MARTHA WASHINGTON

SETTING:

[In the original production a large book was used for the stage setting, size six by four feet. The frame was made of wood, and the pages of beaver board. On the open left-hand page was the frontispiece copied from *The Boy Who Knew What the Birds Said,* illustrated by Padraic Colum. The colors chosen were black, white and deep yellow, done in tempera. The open right-hand page of the book bore the title, THE MAGIC BOOK. The characters entered through the book.]

Book to one side of stage, book case, and table with books on it arranged attractively.

As curtain rises, children are busily engaged examining and discussing the book.

175

[ROBERT *is singing as the curtain rises—busily adding finishing touches to book with painter's brush,* NANCY *and* BERESFORD *looking on*]

BERESFORD: They say it's true but I can hardly believe it. Imagine a magic book and all the characters in the book alive!

NANCY: Oh, but I do believe it, Beresford. With the last stroke of Robert's magic brush—presto!—it is alive. Isn't that the way the story goes, Robert?

ROBERT: True as the truest fairy tale. You see I've dreamed this book all week, and here it is! And I know with my last stroke—[*in a very melodramatic voice*] *Magic!*

BERESFORD: [*puzzled*] You dreamed it?

ROBERT: Yes, the very book. It seems to me I've always dreamed this book. Now, comes the test—will the characters be real? [*excitedly*] Nancy, which characters would you like to see first?

NANCY: Which characters would I like to see? Dear, dear, how difficult to choose. Oh! Oh! I know, I would *adore* to see "Little Women." Oh, we have only to wish, here they come.

BERESFORD: It's too wonderful to be true!

[*Enter* LITTLE WOMEN *and* LAURIE *through page of book, talking as they appear*]

JO: Wouldn't it be fun if all the castles in the air which we make could come true, and we could live in them?

LAURIE: I've made such quantities it would be hard to choose which I'd have.

MEG: You'd have to take your favorite one. What is it?

LAURIE: After I'd seen as much of the world as I want to, I'd like to settle in Germany, and have as much music as I choose. I'm to be a famous musician myself, and live for what I like. That's my favorite castle. What's yours, Meg?

MEG: [*dreamily*] I should like a lovely house full of all sorts of luxurious things,—nice food, pretty clothes, handsome furniture, pleasant people, and heaps of money. I am to be mistress of it, and manage it as I like with plenty of servants, so I never need work a bit. How I should enjoy it, for I shouldn't be idle, but do good and make everybody love me dearly.

LAURIE: [*slyly*] Wouldn't you have a master for your castle in the air?

MEG: [*averting her face and carefully tying her shoe*] I said pleasant people you know.

JO: Why don't you say you'd have a splendid, wise, good husband, and some angelic children? You know your castle wouldn't be perfect without.

MEG: [*petulantly*] You'd have nothing but horses, ink-stands, and novels in yours!

JO: Wouldn't I though? I'd have a stable full of Arabian steeds, rooms piled high with books, and I'd write out of a magic inkstand, so that my works should be as famous as Laurie's music. I want to do something splendid before I go into my castle, something heroic or wonderful that wouldn't be forgotten after I'm dead. I don't know what, but I'm on the watch for it, and mean to astonish you all some day. I think I shall write books and get rich and famous; that would suit me, so that is my favorite dream.

BETH: Mine is to stay at home with father and mother, and help take care of the family.

LAURIE: Don't you wish for anything else?

BETH: Since I have my little piano, I'm perfectly satisfied. I only wish we may all keep well and be together; nothing else.

177

AMY: I have ever so many wishes; but the pet one is to be an artist, and go to Rome, and do fine pictures, and be the best artist in the whole world.

LAURIE: We're an ambitious set, aren't we? Everyone of us, but Beth, wants to be rich, and famous, and gorgeous in every respect. I do wonder if any of us will ever get our wishes.

JO: [*mysteriously*] I've got the key to my castle in the air; but whether I can unlock the door remains to be seen.

LAURIE: I've got the key to mine, but I'm not allowed to try it. Hang college!

AMY: [*waving her pencil*] Here's mine!

MEG: [*forlornly*] I haven't any.

LAURIE: [*at once*] Yes, you have.

MEG: Where?

LAURIE: In your face.

MEG: Nonsense, that's of no use.

LAURIE: [*laughing*] Wait and see if it doesn't bring you something worth having.

JO: [*on way out*] If we are all alive ten years hence, let's meet, and see how many of us have got our wishes, or how much nearer we are than now.

[*Exeunt Little Women and Laurie*]

NANCY: How I love them! They are just as I've always pictured them. I always wished that Jo had married Laurie, didn't you?

BERESFORD: Oh, no, I always thought Amy was so beautiful.

NANCY: Boys, what book do you choose?

BERESFORD: } [*together*] Huck Finn!
ROBERT: } Tom Sawyer!

[TOM SAWYER *and* HUCK FINN *appear*]

TOM: Hello, Huckleberry!

HUCK: Hello, yourself, and see how you like it.

178

Tom: What's that you've got?

Huck: Dead cat.

Tom: Lemme see him Huck. My, he's pretty stiff. Where'd you get him?

Huck: Bought him off a boy.

Tom: What did you give?

Huck: I give a blue ticket and a bladder that I got at the slaughter house.

Tom: Say, what is dead cats good for, Huck?

Huck: Good for? Cure warts with.

Tom: No! Is that so? I know something that's better.

Huck: I bet you don't. What is it?

Tom: Why, spunk water.

Huck: Spunk water! I wouldn't give a dern for spunk-water.

Tom: You wouldn't, wouldn't you? D'you ever try it?

Huck: No I ain't, but Bob Tanner did.

Tom: Who told you so?

Huck: Why he told Jeff Thatcher, and Jeff told Johnny Baker, and Johnny Baker told Jim Hollis, and Jim told Ben Rogers, and Ben told a nigger, and the nigger told me. There now!

Tom: Well, what of it? They'll all lie. Leastaways all except the nigger. I don't know *him*. But I've never seen a nigger that *wouldn't* lie. Shucks! Now tell me how Bob Tanner done it, Huck?

Huck: Why he took and dipped his hand in a rotten stump where the rain water was.

Tom: In the day time?

Huck: Certainly.

Tom: With his face to the stump?

Huck: Yes, least I reckon so.

Tom: Did he say anything?

Huck: I don't reckon he did, I don't know.

179

Tom: Aha! Talk about trying to cure warts with spunk-water in such a blame fool way as that! You got to go all by yourself, to the middle of the wood where you know there's a spunk water stump, and just as it's midnight you back up against the stump and say:
  "Barley corn, Barley corn, injun meal shorts
  Spunk water, spunk water, swaller these warts."
And then walk away quick, eleven steps, with your eyes shut, and then turn around three times and walk home without speaking to anybody. Because if you speak the charm's busted.

Huck: Well that sounds like a good way but that ain't the way Bob Tanner done."

Tom: No sir, you can bet he didn't, becuz' he is the *wartiest* boy in town. But say, how do you cure 'em with dead cats?

Huck: Why you take your cat and go and get in the *graveyard* about midnight when somebody that was *wicked* has been buried; and when it's midnight a devil will come or maybe two or three, but you can't see 'em, you can only hear something like the wind, or maybe hear 'em talk; and when they're taking the fellow away, you heave your cat after 'em and say, "Devil follow corpse, cat follow devil, warts follow cat, I'm done with ye!" That'll fetch *any* wart.

Tom: Sounds good, may I go with you, Huck?

Huck: Of course, if you aren't afraid.
  [*Exit Huck and Tom*]

Robert: I'd like to go with them.

Beresford: I'd like to see Penrod, the big tease.

Penrod: [*running in with sister's letter*] These girls, what perfectly silly letters they write. *This* is a masterpiece and is Sis mad! I expect she'll rush in for this any

180

moment. I got it from her dresser. Imagine her writing this:

"Dear friend,

"You call me beautiful (*giggles*) but I am not *really* beautiful, and there are times when I doubt if I am even pretty, though perhaps my hair is beautiful, and if it is true that my eyes are like blue stars in heaven—"

NANCY: Penrod, stop reading your sister's letter this moment! Aren't you ashamed of yourself?

PENROD: All right, all right, but before she gets *this missive* back I expect the sum total of fifty cents! I must find her now.

NANCY: Hadn't you better change your price to twenty-five cents, you know since this depression I doubt if you'll get your fifty cents.

[*Exit Penrod*]

NANCY: Oh, I have a perfectly marvelous wish!

ROBERT AND BERESFORD: [*dropping to knees with mock gravity*] Yes, Princess, your slightest wish!

NANCY: Oh! Don't be silly—Wouldn't you love to see the Mad Hatter from *Alice in Wonderland*?

[*Enter the* MAD HATTER *and* ALICE]

HATTER: I'm mad, everybody's mad, oh, such a topsy turvey world. The March Hare has never been the same since last March when we quarreled and he went mad. It was at the great concert given by the Queen of Hearts, and I had to sing:

"Twinkle, twinkle, little bat!
How I wonder what you're at!"
"You know the song perhaps?"

ALICE: "I've heard something like it."

181

HATTER: "It goes on, you know, in this way—
            'Up above the world you fly
            Like a tea-tray in the sky'
Well I had hardly finished the first verse when the
Queen bawled out 'He's murdering the time! Off with
his head.' It's always six o'clock now. What day of the
month is it?" [*taking huge watch out of pocket and
looking at it uneasily, shaking it every now and then,
holding it to ear*]

ALICE: [*considering*] The fourth.

HATTER: [*sighing*] Two days wrong. I told the March
Hare that butter would never suit the works! [*to Alice*]
Your hair wants cutting.

ALICE: "You should learn not to make personal remarks,
it's very rude."

HATTER: [*paying no attention to reprimand*] "Why is a
raven like a writing desk?"

ALICE: [*thinking deeply*] I don't know, I give up—What's
the answer?

HATTER: I haven't the slightest idea. I must go. I'm hours
late now. The Queen will be in a rage.
[*Both leave the stage*]

BERESFORD: Do you suppose Old John Silver would step
out of *Treasure Island*?

[*Enter* JOHN SILVER]

JOHN SILVER: "Sixteen men on a dead man's chest.
            Yo ho ho and a bottle of rum."

Here I am—the cruelest, bravest, and cussedest pirate
that ever sailed the main. Scared of me? Everybody's
scared of me. Ah! the things I've done.—I've double
crossed my comrades, I've thieved, and lied.—Even at
that I wager you think I'm the worst and most interesting character in *Treasure Island*. Now, don't you?

182

Everywhere a shudder accompanies my name. I am not afraid of anything. Yo, ho, and a bottle of rum.

[*Exit John Silver*]

NANCY: [*shuddering*] Oh! he frightens me.

ROBERT: Oh! no, he really must have been a very brave man, but of course cruel too. But such adventures. Really I wouldn't have cared to have been John Hawkins in the apple barrel.

NANCY: For my part, I would like to see Little Black Sambo.

[LITTLE BLACK SAMBO *comes rushing in out of breath*]

NANCY: Why, Little Black Sambo, what is the matter? You have been running so hard you are all out of breath.

LITTLE BLACK SAMBO: I'm jus' runnin' away from the tigahs in the jungle. They had taken all my lovely new clothes. Black Mumbo, ma mammy, made me ma beautiful little red coat and ma little blue trousers, and Black Jumbo, ma pappy, gave me ma beautiful green umbrella and purple shoes wif the crimson soles and crimson linings. They had taken them, but wile they were fighting, I put them on agin and how I did run! [*turning to leave*]

BERESFORD: And where are you going now?

LITTLE BLACK SAMBO: Now, now I'se gwine to eat the hundred an' sixty-nine pancakes ma mammy made fo' me.

[*Exit Little Black Sambo*]

BERESFORD: How I should like to see Rebecca of Sunnybrook Farm.

[*Enter* REBECCA *and* EMMA JANE *from "Rebecca of Sunnybrook Farm"*]

REBECCA: Can I sell you a little soap this afternoon? It is called Snow-White and Rose-Red soap, six cakes in an ornamental box, only twenty cents for the white, twenty-five cents for the red. It is made from the purest ingredients, and if desired could be eaten by an invalid with relish.

EMMA JANE: Oh, Rebecca, don't let's say that! [*hysterically*] It makes me feel like a fool!

REBECCA: It takes so little to make you feel like a fool, Emma Jane, that sometimes I think that you must *be* one. I don't get to feeling like a fool so awfully easy; now leave that eating part out if you don't like it and go on.

EMMA JANE: The Snow-White is probably the most remarkable laundry soap ever manufactured. Immerse the garments in a tub, lightly rubbing the more soiled portions with the soap; leave them submerged in water from sunset to sunrise, and then the youngest baby can wash them without the slightest effort.

REBECCA: Babe, not baby.

EMMA JANE: It's the same thing.

REBECCA: Of course, it's just the same *thing*; but a baby has got to be called babe or infant in a circular, the same as it is in poetry! Would you rather say infant?

EMMA JANE: [*grumbling*] No, infant is worse even than babe. Rebecca, do you think we'd better do as the circular says, and let Elijah or Elisha try the soap before we begin selling?

REBECCA: I can't imagine a babe doing a family wash with any soap, but it must be true or they would never dare to print it, so don't let's bother. At some of the houses where they can't possibly know me perhaps I shall say even the last sentence, if I can remember it; "We sound every chord in the great mac-ro-cosm of satisfaction." [*Both leave the stage laughing*]

184

NANCY: Do you suppose we could possibly see Martha and George Washington from Colonial Days?

[*Enter* PAIR *in colonial costume—a minuet—exit*]

ROBERT: That is perfect.

NANCY: These dear friends from Bookland, how I love them. I am eager to meet more delightful people.

ROBERT: I have a marvelous idea, let us follow them into Bookland—I feel certain we shall meet many more friends. Would you like to go?

BERESFORD AND NANCY: We would love to go.

[*Exit through page of book*]

[CURTAIN]

On a Library Shelf
by
Ethelyn Miller

No royalty charged for production

On a Library Shelf

STAGE SET: The curtain opens upon a row of books, one to represent each of the books in the skit, high enough so that the students who are impersonating the characters can stand behind them. Each book must be plainly labeled, and each must have a removable section through which, after the curtain has opened, the student speaks.

BOOKS:

Kidnapped
David Copperfield
Tom Sawyer
Captains Courageous
Anne of Green Gables
Little Women
Captain Blood
Seventeen
Iron Duke

CHARACTERS:

DAVID BALFOUR (*Kidnapped*)
DAVID COPPERFIELD
TOM SAWYER
HARVEY CHEYNE (*Captains Courageous*)
ANNE OF GREEN GABLES
MEG (*Little Women*)
BETH   "   "
JO   "   "
AMY   "   "
CAPTAIN BLOOD
WILLIE BAXTER (*Seventeen*)
JIM WELLINGTON (*Iron Duke*)

DAVID C: Are we alone? Has everybody gone?

TOM S: Yes, the coast is clear. The librarian just locked the door. I heard the key turn. I thought she'd never go.

DAVID C: Now we can talk. Hello, everyone.

CHORUS: Hello.

JIM W: Hello.

WILLIE B: [*stage whisper*] Who is he?

DAVID C: Someone new. A stranger.

CAPT. BLOOD: An upstart? If he is, we'll put him in his place.

JIM W: Hello, hello. You're not a very friendly lot. What are you trying to do? Freeze me out?

DAVID C: Those who prove their worth we welcome. What have you got to say for yourself?

JIM W: Me? Haven't you heard? I'm Jim Wellington of *Iron Duke,* the book that won the New York *Herald Tribune* 1938 Spring Book Award.

CHORUS: So what?

JIM W: I'm good. I know I am. They say that I'm the best college story written since *Stover at Yale.*

DAVID C: Whose brain child are you?

JIM W: John R. Tunis's.

DAVID C: Well, who is he? Some young whippersnapper, I suppose.

JIM W: At any rate, he knows how to write. He's good even if he isn't dead.

DAVID C: I suppose that you had Dickens in mind when you made that last remark.

DAVID B: Who reads you? Anyone?

JIM W: Some do. I admit that I'm not as popular as any of you, but I think that I'm doing all right for myself.

CAPT. BLOOD: [*aside*] It must be his red cover.

TOM S: Let's give him a chance. He wouldn't be here if he wasn't any good at all.

ANNE OF G.G: Yes, I'd like to meet him. We've never been introduced. I'm Anne of Green Gables.

JIM W: How do you do? I'm Jim Wellington. I've heard of you.

190

ANNE OF G.G: Yes—probably how I dyed my hair—but it's no longer green, really.

MEG: Hello, Jim. I'm Meg of *Little Women*. I'll introduce you to my sisters. This is Jo. Oh, dear she isn't here. Never is when I want her. Probably reading a book under a tree. Amy, go find her. Jim, this is Beth.

BETH: I'm the one who dies so peacefully.

JIM W: Do you mind?

BETH: Mind what?

JIM W: Dying?

BETH: Oh, no, the tears that fall upon the pages of my death-bed scene are my reward. I became such a dear and tender memory that I didn't mind being left out of the rest that happens.

MEG: Here is Jo.

JO: Oh, you're a new one. Welcome to our midst. Not a sissy, I hope.

MEG: Jo! This is Amy—the youngest.

AMY: You would add youngest. Jim, I'm the artist of the family. Not a tomboy like Jo.

JIM W: Girls, I've always thought it was wonderful of you to go without your Christmas breakfast so that you could give it to the poor family.

ANNE OF G.G: You wouldn't catch a family of four boys doing that.

TOM: That's enough from you, carrot top.

ANNE OF G.G: The impudence of the creature.

JIM W: Now, Tom, don't arouse Anne's indignation. She might break a slate over your head.

TOM S: Just like a college fellow. Always talking to the girls. Jim, you're among some very famous boys. I'm Tom Sawyer. If you think that your college is the only place, let me tell you about my trip down the Mississippi on a raft.

DAVID C: Oh, Tom, some other time. Jim, I'm David Copperfield.

JIM W: You certainly have a sad life, David.

DAVID C: Yes, Dickens was a little hard on me, but things turn out all right in the end. I do nearly starve to death when I have to earn a living by pasting labels on bottles in a wine shop.

JIM W: Then your great-aunt Betsy Trotwood comes to your aid. You certainly did get to know a host of strange characters. Tell me, is Barkis still "willin' "?

DAVID C: Yes, as long as he's still Barkis.

JIM W: Nurse Peggotty and Mr. Micawber almost "steal the show" from you.

DAVID C: Yes, they almost do.

DAVID B: My name is David, too. David Balfour—and I was kidnapped in 1751.

JIM W: Kidnapping isn't such a modern crime as one would think. Your uncle certainly is a rascal.

DAVID B: Yes, that's a great deal to take from one's own relative. Alan Breck is a splendid chap.

JIM W: But, a little too much mixed up in politics, I should say.

DAVID B: Not politics, my friend—a cause.

JIM W: Have it your own way. I won't argue.

HARVEY C: I'm Harvey Cheyne, Jim, who had such an adventurous trip on a fishing schooner.

JIM W: From what I hear, it did you a lot of good. You certainly were a spoiled brat, before you fell off that liner.

HARVEY C: Yes, I know, but you don't have to rub it in.

JIM W: Sorry. I learned a few things at Harvard myself.

WILLIE: Hello, Jim. I'm Willie. Did you say Harvard?

CAPT. BLOOD: That's what he said, Willie. Maybe Harvard is what you need. The idea, falling for a girl who talks baby talk. She thinks more of her lap-dog

"Flopit" than she'll ever think of you—you itsee witsee Willie.

WILLIE: You're always picking on me, Captain Blood.

CAPT. BLOOD: No more complaints from you or you'll walk the plank.

JIM W: Well, tough guy. Do we get introduced?

CAPT. BLOOD: Well, there's nothing to prevent it, campus celebrity.

WILLIE: Are you really a campus celebrity?

JIM W: [*modestly*] When a fellow breaks the intercollegiate record for the two-mile run, he does get a bit talked about.

WILLIE: I should say so. My life isn't that eventful. That kid sister of mine, Jane, does her best to spoil my plans.

CAPT. BLOOD: Yes, when you tried to borrow your father's dress suit—

WILLIE: You would bring that up.

CAPT. BLOOD: Now, Willie you have much to learn. One voyage on my ship Arabella would open your eyes to a few things. There would be no talking back to me, the master of the waters of the Spanish main.

WILLIE: Don't worry! I won't go traveling with you. Jane would prevent that. She might be doing me a service there.

CAPT. BLOOD: Well, I'm not so sure we'd want you. You'd better go with Tom Sawyer on his raft.

TOM S: Thanks, pal.

JIM W: Boys, may I have the floor?

CAPT. BLOOD: It's yours.

JIM W: I do appreciate your welcome. I won't feel so lonely on these shelves now. Before, I have always been afraid to join in your conversation. You're such famous people. I feel so brand new.

193

Capt. Blood: You won't be that way long—when the students decide they like you. You'll be lucky if you stay in your cover.

Tom S: They'll be turning down the corners of your pages to mark their places.

Jim W: Who's they?

Tom S: The sophomores, probably. Thoughtless lot.

Meg: The girls have a way of leaving such things as combs, hair pins, pencils and chewing gum wrappers as book marks.

Anne of G. G.: And notes, too. I've read some. One—

Meg: [*interrupting*] Never mind.

David C: I hope that you don't have to go through what happened to me. Some football player left me in the locker room. After staying there all night, I was thrown in a corner, stepped on, and torn. I probably would have been thrown away if some kind soul hadn't rescued me.

Anne of G. G.: Some girl was reading me while she was eating lunch. Since then, I've never been able to get rid of that peanut butter she smeared on my pages. I suppose it will wear off in time.

Jim W: Tell me, how does one acquire fame?

Tom S: The movies help. Since Robin Hood went Hollywood he's seldom in. And such airs the fellow has! Heaven knows, he was self-assured enough before his screen success. "Merrie Old England" is hardly large enough to hold him.

Jim W: I don't mean fame like that. I want the boys and girls to like me.

Chorus: They will. Just wait 'til you're a book report.

[Curtain]

194

Nursery Rhymes in A Library Club

by

Mary Eleanor Streeter

No royalty charged for production

Nursery Rhymes in A Library Club

A NONSENSE PLAYLET

TIME: Present.

PLACE: Library of a Junior High School.

CHARACTERS:

BOB, a Junior High School boy.
BO-PEEP
KING COLE
PRETTY MAID
MISS MUFFET
JIM and JERRY, about Bob's age.
A READER
JACK HORNER

SCENE:

A book truck full of books and a table with chairs around it indicate a corner of the Library. At center back hangs a large printed sign: "Library Club—Attention! No meeting here today. Go to Room 311."

[BOB *enters, looks around, evidently not seeing the sign, and puts large armful of school books on table*]

BOB: H'm, where's everyone? Never was the first one anywhere before. Miss Brown's always here. Who ever heard of a library with the librarian missing? And that book report's due Monday. Might as well get right to work at it now. No *Popular Mechanic's Magazine* for little Bobby this afternoon. [*Strolls around, stopping at truck as he finishes speaking*] Well, what do you know! Here's a Mother Goose and in a Junior High Library. [*Picks up book, turning leaves*] Bet Miss Brown didn't know it was here. [*Sits down at table, turning leaves as he speaks*] Haven't seen one of these

197

since I was in First Grade. Wouldn't the fellows love to see this member of the track team reading Mother Goose. Here's a good one to try—[*Reads*] "This chant is said to be good for the hiccoughs, and must be read in one breath to cure." [*Practices on the following rhyme with great speed*]

"Peter Piper picked a peck of pickled peppers;
A peck of pickled peppers Peter Piper picked;
If Peter Piper picked a peck of pickled peppers,
Where's the peck of pickled peppers Peter Piper picked?"

[*Head droops, and as he reads "Sing a song . . . ," the reader takes up the words*]

READER: Sing a song of sixpence, on every side a book,—
    Four and twenty new ones, to make you take a look,
    When the Club assembles each member starts to read
    Of escapades or battles or a hero's valiant deed.
    Some read of airplanes, some of by-gone times;
    Some would sail the ocean blue, but Bob reads nursery rhymes.

BOB: Well, what if I do? There's no one around. [*Raises head*] What on earth made me say that, or did I? [*Goes on turning pages*] Girls sure are different nowadays. Just imagine a girl breaking into print today because she was afraid of spiders. More likely she'd get P in Science if she squealed even once. [*Head droops*]

READER: "Little Miss Muffet—"

[MISS MUFFET *enters, sits on a tuffet and reads until a large spider is pulled across the stage near her*]

    Little Miss Muffet
    Sits on her tuffet
    Reading her book every day.

Miss Muffet: The tales are so thrilling
To stop I'm not willing [*Rises and leaves stage with nose in book*]
Go away, silly spider, go 'way.

[*Pretty Maid enters from opposite side*]

Reader: Where are you going, my pretty maid?

Maid: I've come to the Library Club today.

Reader: May I come with you, my pretty maid?

Maid: If you'll read with me, of course you may.

Reader: And what are you reading, my pretty maid?

Maid: I'm reading adventures and romances gay.

Reader: Then I'll come with you, my pretty maid,
And in this Library I'll surely stay.

[*Maid slips out as Bob stretches, rubs his eyes, etc.*]

Bob: Library Club, huh! What—Who said that? Where on earth are the rest of the bunch? I must have gotten up here in nothing flat—or else class let out early. [*Turns leaves*] Gee, these take me back to my childhood —Old King Cole, and Jack and Jill, and Little Bo-Peep. "Little Bo-Peep has lost her sheep—" [*His voice trails off*]

Bo-Peep: [*stepping from behind curtain, or coming up from below the platform or stage*]
Don't believe him!
I'm Little Bo-Peep—I haven't many sheep,
And I don't have to mind them.
I just read my book, in some quiet nook,
While the sheep wag their tails behind them.

[*Goes off stage with nose in book, as King Cole strides in*]

Bob: [*Mutters, with his head still in his arms*]
"Old King Cole was a merry old soul
And a merry old soul was he—"

199

KING COLE: Come bring my chair [*silence*]
           [*Shouts*] Come—bring—my—chair! [*Pretty Maid comes with one which she places in a corner*]
           And my spectacles, too, [*Bo-Peep brings huge ones*]
           And bring me my new books three, [*Reader comes with them*]
           I'll read my story, 'tis wild and gory,
           And a very fine story, you see.
           For there's none so rare as can compare
           With King Cole and his story books three.
[*King Cole retires to his corner, and remains there reading until the curtain falls*]

BOB: [*Mumbles*] "Jack and Jill went up the. . ."
[*Junior High School boy and girl bounce in*]

JIM: ⎱
JERRY: ⎰ [*together*] Here we are, not Jack and Jill, but—

READER: 'Tis young Jim and Jerry
           Come to the Library
           To find a book for pleasure.

JERRY: That rhyme's awful!

JIM: Silence, friend—the rhyme may be awful—but it is beautiful compared to the meter!

READER: As I was saying,—
           'Tis young Jim and Jerry
           Come to the Li-*brar*-y,
           To find some books for pleasure.
           Jim found one, and home did run,
           Now Jerry's found a treasure.
[*Jim and Jerry suit action to Reader's words, and then bounce off the stage*]

BOB: [*sitting up*] Funny how childish these rhymes seem at my age. Silly—this one. [*Begins to say "Little Jack Horner" as fast as he can say it*]

READER: Stop! [*Points finger at Bob. JACK HORNER comes on, and he points his finger at Bob, also*] Stop! You're wrong, young man!

READER: }
JACK HORNER: } [*together*]

You're *big Bob* Horner, you sat in your corner
Reading a nursery rhyme book.
You looked round with glee,
Your late club friends to see—
Ha, ha—how funny you look.

BOB: [*Jumps up, wide awake*] I've had enough of this. Either I'm hearing things, or I've been dreaming. [*Looks around*] There isn't any Library Club here, and the Librarian has not come in since I got here. [*Suddenly sees sign*] Well—for—[*Walks over, touches sign to see if it is real*] "Library Club,—attention! No meeting here today. Go to Room 311." And I've been here alone all this time. [*Sees King Cole*] No,—he can't be real! This is what I get for reading Mother Goose. [*Picks up books, runs off, being careful to keep a good distance from King Cole*] I'm getting out of here!

[CURTAIN]

201

A Night in the Library

by

Raymond Higdon and Helen Hanke

No royalty charged for production

This play was written by two of the students of the Edison Senior High School, Miami, Florida and presented in the School Assembly, by the Miami Edison Library Club.

CHARACTERS:
> BILL: A senior in high school who spends his time sleeping and drawing in books
> MARY: Bill's glamour girl
> JACK: The smart aleck of the senior class
> IRENE: Jack's girl
> MRS. TIGHTLIP: The school librarian—a replica of days gone by
> A group of students
> THE SLANG DICTIONARY
> VOL. 23 OF THE AMERICAN ENCYCLOPEDIA
> CONCISE BIOGRAPHICAL DICTIONARY
> GEORGE WASHINGTON
> ABE LINCOLN
> MARY, QUEEN OF SCOTLAND

STAGE SETTING: The stage is set to resemble the school library. Book cases line the walls with the reference section commanding the rear center position. Library tables and chairs are spaced in a manner not to interfere with Mrs. Tightlip's desk at right mid-stage.

COSTUMES:

Scene 1

STUDENTS: School attire.
MRS. TIGHTLIP: Black dress with white collar, flat heeled shoes and horn rimmed glasses.

Scene 2

SLANG DICTIONARY: Two large pieces of orange poster paper worn in "sandwich-man" manner. Book title lettered in black.
AMERICANA ENCYCLOPEDIA: Two extra large sheets of royal blue poster paper with book title lettered in yellow.
CONCISE BIOGRAPHICAL DICTIONARY: Big red book made from poster paper and ply wood. Concise biographical dictionary, himself, is seated inside with only head showing. One side of book swings open enough for characters to spring forth.
ABE LINCOLN: Black suit, white shirt with soft silk tie; Pipe. Bald head effect may be created by using the top of a beige hose pulled over the head in scull-cap fashion.

GEORGE WASHINGTON: Conventional George Washington attire, supplemented by glasses, beard, and comic hat.

MARY, QUEEN OF SCOTLAND: Black velvet dress with cape thrown over her head. A huge white pleated collar is placed around her head to give the effect of being headless. (At last minute this costume caused trouble and a large black sign with "No Head" lettered in white was substituted. This gag went over in a big way)

Scene 3

Same as Scene 1, with the exception of Bill.

BILL: Crutches, arm in sling, cuts and bruises.

A Night in the Library

SCENE I

TIME: 2:15 in the afternoon.
PLACE: The Library of Meadow Lane High School.
  Bill, Jack and Irene are seated at one of the tables. The library is full of students. Mrs. Tightlip is busy at the charge desk.

JACK: How was your blind date last night?

BILL: Humph—it was blind all right.

IRENE: Why, what was wrong with her?

BILL: Oh, nothing. Her face just looked like the front end of a Mack truck. That's all.

[*At this point a student starts to sit in the one vacant chair at the table*]

JACK: Hey! This chair's saved. You'd better sit somewhere else.

[*The student walks away and finds another seat*]

IRENE: Where is Mary, Bill?

BILL: I don't know. She said she'd be right in.

[MARY *enters from the left*]

JACK: Here she comes now.

[*Mary walks over, blowing on her nails on her right hand. She has just polished them. She sits in the empty chair*]

BILL: What took you so long, Mary?

MARY: I had to polish my nails for tonight. Aren't they pretty?

[*She displays her bright red nails proudly*]

BILL: That's right, we are going to the dance tonight. Would you like to go, Jack? You and Irene?

207

JACK: That suits me. What about you, Irene?

IRENE: You bet, I'd love it!

[*Just then Mrs. Tightlip walks over*]

MRS. TIGHTLIP: You must stop this talking in the library. I'll have to send you back to study hall if you continue.

JACK: [*innocently*] Talking? We weren't talking.

[*Mrs. Tightlip says nothing but backs away watching them. She turns to give her attention to another table of students. Jack, Irene, Bill and Mary begin reading. Jack can stand it no longer so he slips a pin from his pocket and sticks Irene*]

IRENE: [*loudly*] Ouch!

[*Jack starts to read and looks perfectly innocent. Mrs. Tightlip turns around and seeing everyone looking at that table, she walks over*]

MRS. TIGHTLIP: Who did that?

JACK: Did what?

MRS. TIGHTLIP: Made that noise.

JACK: What noise? I didn't hear any noise, did you, Irene?

IRENE: [*trying to keep a straight face*] No, I didn't hear a thing.

MRS. TIGHTLIP: You [*pointing to Jack*] and Irene had better go back to Study Hall.

[*Jack and Irene get up and leave together. On the way out Jack clips a fellow student on the head. This action takes place behind Mrs. Tightlip's back*]

MARY: Say, I'd better go back and get my algebra. Old lady Addup said she would flunk me if I didn't have my home work today.

BILL: That old so and so! She's mean enough to do anything.

MARY: I'll see you tonight about a quarter to nine.

BILL: Okay.

[*Mary leaves and Bill begins to get sleepy, laying his head on the table. Students begin leaving the library. Mrs. Tightlip goes over, shakes Bill, motioning for him to leave. He falls back to sleep. She appears not to notice. When the chairs are in place and the books on the shelves, she leaves*]

[CURTAIN]

SCENE II

TIME: Almost midnight.

PLACE: Same.

As curtain rises, we find Bill still asleep. A clock in the distance strikes twelve. Bill begins to show signs of waking up. Just as the clock finishes striking, a strange light fills the library. Bill glances around rubbing his eyes. He notices some of the books moving around. These books have increased in proportion and have taken on certain human aspects such as heads, arms, legs and—what ho!—they talk. Bill keeps very quiet and still, being too amazed to do otherwise.

SLANG DICTIONARY: Hi-yah-ya, old stuck up. Am I or am I not in the groove tonight?

VOL. 23: I haven't been able to sleep all night.

SLANG DICTIONARY: What's da matter witcha, Babe?

VOL. 23: Oh, some boy tore that illustration of Rome from me. When he did, it cut off my circulation. I simply don't know what I'm going to do!

SLANG DICTIONARY: [*talking to Concise biographical dictionary who is still trying to get off the shelf*] What seems to be eating on ya, Toots?

BIOGRAPHICAL DICTIONARY: If you'd take a look inside me, you wouldn't ask me what was wrong.

SLANG DICTIONARY: Tanks! Don't mind if I do.

209

VOL. 23: I'll open the cover and you can look inside.

[*Just as he is about to open it, it opens by itself. A figure steps out. It is* GEORGE WASHINGTON. *He has a beard, a funny hat, and a pair of glasses. As he steps out, the Slang dictionary jumps back in surprise*]

SLANG DICTIONARY: Say Bud, where'd you pop from?

GEORGE W.: I am George Washington, the first President of the United States.

VOL. 23: You don't resemble the pictures I have seen of him.

GEORGE W.: How true, how true. I always hated beards and I never wore glasses, except when reading. But I am forced to wear them all the time now, just because some would-be artist puts them there in my picture.

SLANG DICTIONARY: You sure got the dirty end of the deal that time, Georgy.

[*Just then another figure can be seen stepping out of the Concise biographical dictionary. It is* ABE LINCOLN]

ABE LINCOLN: Friends, Romans, and Countrymen, lend me your ears, mine are dirty.

VOL. 23: Certainly not a well-spoken fellow, is he? Who is he?

SLANG DICTIONARY: Humph—your guess is as good as mine. Ask him. He looks like Old Man Mose to me.

VOL. 23: [*To Abe Lincoln*] Who are you?

ABE LINCOLN: I am Abe Lincoln, one of the greatest men in American history.

VOL. 23: But I never heard that speech of yours before. When did you make it?

SLANG DICTIONARY: [*muttering loudly to himself and shaking his head*] Abe Lincoln wit a pipe, without any hair on his head. *Dat's terrific*!

ABE LINCOLN: These changes in my appearance are the results of many beauty treatments that I have received from people who think they know how I should look.

VOL. 23: But what happened to your ear?

ABE LINCOLN: A boy tore it off to throw at a friend of his.

SLANG DICTIONARY: I think we oughter get together and find out who is doing all this damage. Don't you? [*He looks around at all of them*]

VOL. 23: I quite agree with you!
[*Here the conversation is interrupted by the appearance of a headless lady (MARY, QUEEN OF SCOTS). Her neck is clothed in a stiff white collar and a black bow tie*]

VOL. 23: Look at this [*He points to the moving figure*]

SLANG DICTIONARY: Dis ain't a dream, is it?

VOL. 23: Who are you?

FIGURE: I am Mary, Queen of Scotland.

SLANG DICTIONARY: Den I'm Yahoody.

MARY: I realize that I am a little disfigured, but what can I do when students insist on chopping off my head, pages before I am to be beheaded?

SLANG DICTIONARY: Don't ask me.

VOL. 23: I think we should find some way to punish students who do things like that.

ALL OTHERS: *Me, too! So do I! You betcha!*

ABE LINCOLN: I wish I could lay my hands on one of them. [*He turns and sees Bill*] There's one of them. Let's chastise him! [*They all start for Bill. He tries to get away, but is too late*]

VOL. 23: Stop his circulation!

ABE LINCOLN: Tear his ear off!

MARY: Chop his head off!

GEORGE W.: I'm going to shave off his hair.

SLANG DICTIONARY: Hold on. Not so fast! Take him outside, so we won't mess up the library.

GEORGE W.: That is a splendid suggestion.
[*They pick him up bodily and carry him out, while the curtain goes down*]

211

SCENE III

TIME: Next day.
PLACE: Same.

When the curtain rises, Mary, Irene and Jack are sitting at one of the tables, talking. Mrs. Tightlip is at the charge desk.

JACK: I wonder where Bill was last night?

IRENE: I don't know.

MARY: I'd sure like to get my fingers around his neck right now. Stand me up, will he. Humph, I'll show him a thing or two.

[*Just then* BILL *comes limping in on crutches. He is all bandaged, ear patched, neck bruised, hair disheveled, arm in a sling*]

JACK: Hey! Here comes Bill now. Look at him.

MARY: What on earth happened to him?

[*Bill ignores them and goes directly to Mrs. Tightlip*]

BILL: Is the Slang dictionary in? Are you sure?

MRS. TIGHTLIP: Yes, of course it is. Reference section no. 420, but what on earth has happened to you?

BILL: Never mind what happened to me. Was Vol. 23, of the Americana here this morning when you opened up? And that book about famous folks?

[*As Bill is talking rather loudly, the other students overhear his request and bring the books to him. Bill sees the books, jumps back and after a moment makes himself feel them. The students are looking curiously at him, until he finally musters enough courage to speak*]

BILL: Mrs. Tightlip, may I speak to the students?

MRS. TIGHTLIP: You may, as I am as eager to hear what has happened as they are.

BILL: I got the stuffin' beat out of me last night by those books! [*Students laugh and make fun of him*] It is not funny and it is the truth! I fell asleep here yesterday and was awakened at midnight by the hullabaloo

made by the characters in these books. They were rais-
ing Cain about the way we treat them. When they spied
me—they did everything to me that had been done to
them! My only escape was by promising to tell you that
the same thing would happen to you if you don't begin
treating our library books better.

[*Steps down stage and recites to the audience as curtain
is slowing closing*]

I'm a living picture as you can see
Of what these books have done to me.
So take my advice and heed my plea
Or fate will do this thing to thee!

[CURTAIN]

213

Thou Shalt Not Read

by

Mary Margaret Hursey

CHARACTERS:

    NANCY JO, the girl who hated to read.
    HER MOTHER
    THE THREE MUSKETEERS
    ROBIN HOOD
    THE THREE WITCHES
    PINOCCHIO
    HUMPTY DUMPTY
    TOM SAWYER
    HAMLET
    PORTIA
    MOTHER GOOSE
    TOMMY ATKINS, Kipling's typical soldier in India.
    ALICE IN WONDERLAND
    RAVEN

This play was written by a senior student (class of 1941), Mary Margaret Hursey, and presented by the Library Club of the Coshocton High School during Book Week in November, 1940.

The following notes concerning it were contributed by Marjorie L. Rogers, Librarian, Coshocton High School, Coshocton, Ohio

"*About the players*: Every class in school was represented in the play, from freshmen to seniors. Some were members of the Library Club, some were not. We deliberately tried to have a cross-section of the student body.

"*About the costumes*: We did not try to plan elaborate costumes perfect in every detail, although some students went to more trouble than others. Our aim was merely to suggest the characters by a few characteristic bits of clothing. Hamlet, Portia and the Raven wore black choir robes. Other parts of Hamlet's costume were a black cambric dickey with white cheese-cloth neck ruching, tight sleeves made from black cotton stockings with the feet cut off and ruching sewn in at the wrists, large locket and chain. Portia's cap was a berry basket covered with black crêpe paper. The Raven wore a black cambric hood with a large yellow beak and huge black crêpe paper wings made by the Art Department and worn on the arms, shield fashion, so that he could flap them. The Three Musketeers wore capes, large-brimmed women's felt hats with plumes, arctics left unhooked, crêpe paper wigs (yellow, rust and black) made on old felt hat crowns used as foundation, and grease paint mustaches. They carried rapiers constructed by the Industrial Arts Department from tapered dowel sticks and coffee can lids. The witches wore gray blankets and stringy gray and white wigs. The costumes of Pinocchio, Robin Hood and Mother Goose were colorful and fairly complete as to detail. Tom Sawyer lacked a straw hat.

"*About the production*: We did not rewrite or remodel the play in any way. A darkened stage with occasional flashes of light and backstage rumbling, to simulate lightning and thunder, heightened the dramatic effect during the appearances of the witches. Mother Goose's "goose" practiced with the cast and did not break up the show. No one found his lines difficult to learn. The playlet requires from fifteen to twenty minutes. We followed its presentation with the reading by one of the English teachers of several passages from *A Tale of Two Cities*, Nancy Jo's 'required reading.'

"The school librarian might prepare a group of the books suggested by some of the characters in the play and immediately after the skit display them prominently with such slogans as 'Meet the stars,' 'We were in the play. Here we are in person,' et cetera."

Thou Shalt Not Read

ACT I

TIME: Present.

SCENE: An ordinary living room. MOTHER is reading in a chair. [*Suddenly the door opens and in comes* NANCY JO. *She slams her books on the table. There is a book lying on the table and when she sees it, she turns her head with a groan of disgust*]

NANCY JO: Oh, darn it!

MOTHER: [*looking up*] Why, what's the matter, dear?

NANCY JO: Oh, every time I come into this room, there's that darn book staring me in the face.

MOTHER: What book?

NANCY JO: Oh, that horrible old *Tale of Two Cities!* I'm getting so sick of it. I don't see why we have to read such dry old books for school.

MOTHER: Why, Nancy Jo! You should be glad you have the opportunity to read so many good books.

NANCY JO: Good books! Did I hear you say good books? For Heaven's sake, Mother, they're all so dry I can't even keep awake while I read them. And besides, they're all so long. It takes forever to finish one. By the time I get to the end, I forget what happened in the beginning.

MOTHER: I don't think it's so bad as all that, Nancy Jo. When do you have to have it read?

NANCY JO: Next Tuesday. Oh, I wish I didn't have to read it!

MOTHER: How far are you?

NANCY JO: I've been reading and reading and I'm only to page 92.

MOTHER: [*rising*] Now you must settle right down and get busy. You have only four more days to finish it. Why don't you read a couple of chapters right now before supper?

NANCY JO: Oh, Mother, can't I even have a minute's peace? I don't have time to read. And anyway, I don't like to read. I *hate* to read, in fact!

MOTHER: Now you sit right down there and start on that book. I won't have a daughter of mine talking like that. [*Points to davenport*]

NANCY JO: Oh, Mother—

MOTHER: Sit right down there, young lady!

NANCY JO: [*grumbling*] Oh, all right.

[*Mother leaves, but before she goes out the door, she turns to see that Nancy is doing as she is told. Nancy Jo settles herself comfortably on the davenport and opens the book*]

NANCY JO: Oh, darn it, anyway. This book makes me sleepy even to look at it!

[*Reads a little, yawns, and turns the page*]

[CURTAIN]

ACT II

TIME: Immediately after Act I.

SCENE: Same as Act I. NANCY JO is asleep on the davenport. The stage is darker than in Act I.

[*The* THREE WITCHES *file in.* NANCY JO *rouses up when they begin to speak*]

FIRST WITCH: When shall we three meet again
                In thunder, lightning, or in rain?

SECOND WITCH: When the hurly-burly's done,
     When Nancy Jo has lost and won.
THIRD WITCH: That shall be ere set of sun.
FIRST WITCH: Where the place?
SECOND WITCH: Right in this room.
THIRD WITCH: Here Nancy Jo shall meet her doom.
FIRST WITCH: I come, Graymalkin!
SECOND WITCH: Paddock calls.
THIRD WITCH: Anon.
ALL: Fair is foul, and foul is fair:
     They shall do all that they do dare.
     [*All file out to other side of stage. Stage is lighted up
     again*]
NANCY JO: [*shaking*] Who-what-what do they mean?
     Who are they?
     [*Enter the* THREE MUSKETEERS. *They stop in the
     middle of the room and clash their swords together*]
SECOND MUSKETEER: Remember!
ALL: All for one and one for all!
     [*Clash swords together again. All about face and see
     Nancy Jo*]
FIRST MUSKETEER: [*Points*] Aha! Yon sits fair culprit!
SECOND MUSKETEER: And doubtless more evil than she
     appears to be!
THIRD MUSKETEER: Surround her, men! She is a trick
     wench!
NANCY JO: W-who are you? What have *I* done?
FIRST MUSKETEER: Ho! She asks what she has done!
SECOND MUSKETEER: We are the Three Musketeers!
THIRD MUSKETEER: Arise, and come with us!
NANCY JO: But where are you taking me?
     [*Two of the Musketeers seize her arms*]
NANCY JO: Let me go! Help!
     [ROBIN HOOD *enters, sights with his hands*]

221

ROBIN HOOD: What do I spy? Aha! A fair damsel in distress! Robin Hood to the rescue! [*Advances to group*] Avast, ye pirates! Unhand this fair maiden!

FIRST MUSKETEER: Avast yourself! Who dares challenge the Three Musketeers?

SECOND MUSKETEER: Silence! All of you! Sir, who are you?

ROBIN HOOD: Robin Hood! Coming to the rescue of a fair maiden in distress! And who are you who so glibly assume command?

SECOND MUSKETEER: We are the Three Musketeers. And this fair maiden in distress is none other than Nancy Jo!

ROBIN HOOD: Nancy Jo! The wench who—!

THIRD MUSKETEER: Aye! The wench who denounces books!

ROBIN HOOD: Well! That's a horse of a different color! Come! What are we waiting for? Let's go!
[*Seizes her arm. One Musketeer still is holding her other arm and one steps in front of her and one behind. They start marching across the stage. Nancy Jo, of course, resists, but to no avail. Just then* PINOCCHIO *runs in followed by* HUMPTY DUMPTY]

PINOCCHIO: Stay here! They're going to have the trial right here.

HUMPTY DUMPTY: Yes! Hamlet said to tell you. And he said to fix up a place for the trial.

FIRST MUSKETEER: What! Soldiers stoop to menial labor? Who does he think he is, ordering us about?

SECOND MUSKETEER: Go back and tell him we must guard the culprit.

PINOCCHIO: Does it take four big men just to guard one little girl?

THIRD MUSKETEER: Why you impudent young—

Robin Hood: Hold on! My keen ears hear bare feet approaching!

[*Enter* Tom Sawyer]

Tom: What's the matter with you guys?

Humpty Dumpty: Hamlet wants them to fix a place for the trial and they won't do it because they are soldiers. [*Guards seat Nancy Jo in a chair and range themselves around her. Tom starts shifting furniture around, and Pinocchio and Humpty Dumpty watch him interestedly. He moves the table, puts a chair behind it and one beside it, and fixes the other chairs for an audience. Enter* Hamlet *followed by* Portia *and* Mother Goose. *Hamlet immediately takes chair behind table. Mother Goose and Portia take seats on the davenport. Pinocchio and Humpty Dumpty sit on a little table*]

Mother Goose: [*looking at Nancy Jo*] Poor dear! I'm sure she didn't *mean* to do wrong.

Portia: She was very wicked and deserves no pity whatsoever!

Mother Goose: Oh yes! But don't deal *too* harshly with her. Remember, you were once a girl yourself.

Portia: [*hesitating*] We shall see. We shall see.

[*Enter* Tommy Atkins *and* Alice in Wonderland]

Tommy: We 'eard there was going to be a trial 'ere, hand thot we'd drop by hand see hit.

Alice: That's a pretty serious offence, isn't it?

Nancy Jo: What's a pretty serious offence? What did I do that was so terrible? Won't someone *please* explain!

Tommy: [*looking at her*] So! This is the wicked criminal. Hmm!

Alice: [*Seated, whispers to Mother Goose*] She's not so very much older than I am, is she?

223

Mother Goose: No, dear, and now let's be quiet. I think they're going to start.

[*Portia has been talking to the judge, Hamlet. Tommy has been talking to the guards and stays with them*]

Pinocchio: Let's get started!

Humpty Dumpty: Yeah! C'mon!

Hamlet: [*Raps gavel*] Order in the court—order in the court! To acquit Nancy Jo or not to acquit Nancy Jo; that is the question. Miss Portia will represent the books' side and Miss Nancy Jo, have you an attorney?

Nancy Jo: No.

Hamlet: [*severely*] Your Honor.

Nancy Jo: No, *Your Honor,* I will defend myself.

Hamlet: Very well. Proceed, Miss Portia.

Portia: Honorable Judge and interested friends: As you all know, this trial is being held to ascertain whether or not this young lady [*Points to Nancy Jo*] blasphemed books and reading.

Nancy Jo: I—

Portia: Quiet, please. Bring the defendant to the chair. [*The Three Musketeers, Robin Hood, and Tommy Atkins all march up with Nancy Jo, about face and retreat. Nancy Jo sits in witness chair beside table*]

Portia: Swear to tell the truth, the whole truth, and nothing but the truth, so help you God?

Nancy Jo: I do.

Portia: Your name?

Nancy Jo: Nancy Jo.

Portia: Residence?

Nancy Jo: Right here.

Portia: Age?

Nancy Jo: Fifteen.

Portia: Very well. Now will you please tell us where you were an hour ago?

Nancy Jo: In this very room.

224

PORTIA: What were you doing?

NANCY JO: Talking to Mother.

PORTIA: What about?

NANCY JO: Oh—books, I guess.

PORTIA: Is it true that you said you hated to read?

NANCY JO: I-I guess so.

PORTIA: Yes or no!

NANCY JO: Yes.

PORTIA: Did you say you hated books, also?

NANCY JO: I didn't mean it! Honest, I didn't!

PORTIA: Just answer the question, please.

NANCY JO: [*sullenly*] Yes, then.

[*Everyone gasps and looks shocked*]

PORTIA: [*sternly*] Now what have you to say for yourself?

NANCY JO: [*angrily*] Only this—what do *you* care whether I like books or not? It's none of your business! This whole thing is just too silly for words! I *hate* to read! And what's more, I'll *never* read another line! And you can't make me! So there! [*Turns up nose*]

[*Everyone is shocked into a complete silence for a little bit*]

MOTHER GOOSE: [*shaking her head sadly*] I never would have believed it. That poor young girl.

ROBIN HOOD: She's even worse than I thought.

[*The Three Musketeers march up to Hamlet*]

FIRST MUSKETEER: We refuse to remain in the vicinity of such a wicked person.

SECOND MUSKETEER: We recommend *no* mercy.

THIRD MUSKETEER: Remember!

ALL THREE MUSKETEERS: It's All for One and One for All! [*Clang swords together*] Adieu! [*March out*]

TOM: Well—that's that!

PORTIA: Honorable Judge, I believe you can easily see that she is guilty. In fact, she admits it herself. Therefore, I suggest that you sentence her to a severe penalty. In-

225

deed, a pound of flesh would not be too severe in this case. [*Sits down*]

NANCY JO: Oh, no! no! That would *kill* me!

HAMLET: To kill or not to kill; that is the question.

MOTHER GOOSE: [*rising*] Honorable Judge, I don't think we need to be so severe. Why don't you sentence her to a life without reading? That wouldn't kill her, yet it would be hard to endure.

HAMLET: Ah, *excellent*! The perfect punishment!

NANCY JO: Ha! That wouldn't be punishment! That would be joy!

PORTIA: [*ignoring her*] Yes, the perfect punishment. But how can we inflict it? We *can't* keep her from reading. [*Everyone puzzles about it for awhile. Enter the* THREE WITCHES]

ALL THE WITCHES: [*chanting*]
>   Double, double, toil and trouble!
>   As you think, the task grows double!

FIRST WITCH: We can solve your problem sad
>   For we are bad, oh *very* bad.

SECOND WITCH: Nancy shall not read again,
>   For we can stop her, *hark ye,* then!

THIRD WITCH: Over her we'll cast a spell,
>   And she'll not read, for Heaven or Hell.
[*One of the Witches seizes her, and they all dance around her*]

WITCHES: Double, double, toil and trouble
>   As you think, the task grows double!

FIRST WITCH: One times three is three times one
>   And three times three is nine.
>   Nine times nine is eighty-one,
>   So drink ye now this mystick wine!
[*Forces Nancy Jo to drink something out of a flask*]

WITCHES: Double, double, toil and trouble
>   Our feet burn, and the wine does bubble!

[*Second Witch repeats same performance as First Witch*]

WITCHES: Double, double, toil and trouble
This spell *cannot* be broken as a bubble!

[*Third Witch repeats same performance as other two Witches*]

WITCHES: Double, double, toil and trouble
The spell is cast; now you'll have trouble!

[*Witches dance around her several times chanting, "Now you'll have trouble—now you'll have trouble!" Then they dance right on out of the room*]

NANCY JO: [*Looks frightened for a little bit, and then says*] Whew!

HAMLET: And thus you are sentenced to a life without reading.

NANCY JO: Oh, that's a lot of hooey. I don't feel any different. And besides, I don't like to read anyway.

HAMLET: So be it. [*Goes out*]

PORTIA: So be it. [*Goes out*]

MOTHER GOOSE: So be it. [*Goes out*]

ROBIN HOOD: So be it. [*Goes out*]

ALICE: So be it. [*Goes out*]

PINOCCHIO: So be it. [*Goes out*]

HUMPTY DUMPTY: So be it. [*Goes out*]

NANCY JO: So what! [*Goes over to davenport*]

[*Tom Sawyer and Tommy Atkins are at the back of the room and she doesn't notice them until Tom Sawyer comes over to her*]

TOM: You lucky so and so!

NANCY JO: Lucky!

TOM: Yes! Just think, now you won't even have to go to school.

NANCY JO: [*rising*] Not have to go to school? Why?

TOM: Well, if you can't read, you can't very well study, can you?

227

NANCY JO: Oh, that's a lot of bunk. I can too read. And I'll still go to school. Why I *want* to go to school! I *like* school!

TOM: Gee, you're in a pretty bad way. Like to go to school. [*Pauses*] How do you know you can read?

NANCY JO: [*sitting down*] Just bring me that book and I'll prove it.

TOM: [*handing her the book*] Here ya are.

NANCY JO: [*Tries to open it*] Why what's the matter with this darn book? It won't open! Look! [*Tugs at it to no avail*]

TOM: Let me see. [*Takes book and opens it easily*] You're crazy. There's nothing wrong with it.

NANCY JO: Here. [*Tries to open it again and still can't open it*] Why it won't open for me! Maybe I can open this one. [*Drops book on floor and gets another*] It won't open either!

TOM: It opens for me. [*Opens it*] See?

NANCY JO: [*astonished*] Why—! [*Gets out a lot of books and tries to open them. None will open for her but they do for Tom*] You'd think they were bewitched!

TOM: And so they are. Remember? Those old witches certainly fixed you!

NANCY JO: [*Ponders awhile*] Oh, that's impossible! I never heard tell of such a thing. I'm not superstitious anyway. And why don't you go home? You bother me! And besides, I don't like to read anyway, so there!

TOM: It's a good thing you don't. Well, I guess I'll go. So long! [*Goes out whistling*]

NANCY JO: [*sinking into chair*] This is all just a dream. I'll wake up in a minute. I *know* I will. [*Rubs eyes. Looks over and sees Tommy Atkins still sitting*] Why you're still here! What do you want? Why don't you go home and let me alone?

[*Tommy gets up and starts walking back and forth in a
slow manner repeating*—]

TOMMY:

Books-books-books-books-all kinds and types of books.
We're read—read—read—read—readin' in America——
Books—books—books—books—all kinds and types of
    books.
        But *you'll* never read them anymore.
Fiction — biography — history — travel — all kinds and
    types of books.
Fiction — biography — history — travel — all kinds and
    types of books.
You—you—you—you—you'll go mad at seein' 'em.
        But *you'll* never read them anymore.
Don't—don't—don't—don't—even try to open one.
Books—books—books—books—all kinds and types of
    books.
You—you—you—you—you'll go mad at seein' 'em.
        But *you'll* never read them anymore.
You'll—try—try—try—try—to open and read one.
Books—books—books—books—You'll go mad at seein'
    'em.
Books—books—books—books—all kinds and types of
    books.
        But *you'll* never read them anymore.

Books—books—books—books—

NANCY JO: [*jumping up*] For heaven's sake get out of
here before I kick you out! *Get out*! I say! *Get out*
[*Chases him out*] I'll go crazy if this keeps up! [*Pauses*]
Guess I'll just rest a minute. [*Sits down and mops fore-
head with handkerchief*]
[*Someone knocks on the door*]

NANCY JO: Now who could that be? [*Opens door and the*
RAVEN *walks in*]

229

NANCY JO: Who are you? [*No answer. Raven just stands*] What do you want? [*No answer*] Can't you even talk? [*No answer*] You must be Poe's "Raven"! Oh Heavens! Not that! Anything but that! [*Groans*] What do you want, Raven?—[*pause*] Why don't you say something? [*pause. Nancy Jo turns away in despair*] Oh, why do I have to be bothered so much? Can't you go and let me die in peace? [*turning*] *Go away!*

RAVEN: Nevermore.

NANCY JO: [*Starts*] Oh, so you can talk. Well in that case I'll just ignore you. [*Sits down*] Guess I'll just read a book. [*Picks up a book*]

RAVEN: Nevermore.

NANCY JO: [*Startled again*] What? [*pause*] Oh, maybe I'm hearing things. I'm so nervous I don't know whether I'm coming or going. [*Tries to open book*] Oh, darn it! These awful old books won't even open yet.

RAVEN: Nevermore.

NANCY JO: Will you please be quiet? Can't you see that I'm nervous?

RAVEN: Nevermore.

NANCY JO: [*disgusted*] Oh, all right. Have it your own way. [*Turns away*] At least I can read a newspaper. The front page anyway. [*Picks up paper*] Oh darn it. The print's all blurry and I can't make it out. Why, it's black magic! Can't I even read newspapers?

RAVEN: Nevermore.

NANCY JO: Do I have to go through life without reading? Can't I read *anything*?

RAVEN: Nevermore.

NANCY JO: Oh, why did I say I hated to read? I *have* to read! I can't live without reading! I just *must* read!

RAVEN: Nevermore.

NANCY JO: [*turning to him in a fury*] And you, Raven, shut up! I can't stand it. *Shut up!*

RAVEN: Nevermore.

NANCY JO: Well take this! and this! [*Throws two books at him. The Raven chases her around and around the room saying "Nevermore" all the while. Finally she jumps onto the sofa, hides her head in the pillows and shouts*]

NANCY JO: Help! Mother! Help! Help!

RAVEN: Nevermore. [*Pulls her off sofa*]

[CURTAIN]

ACT III

TIME: Immediately after Act II.
SCENE: Same as before.

[NANCY JO *is on the floor beside the sofa, and* MOTHER *is shaking her*]

MOTHER: Nancy Jo! Wake up! Wake up!

NANCY JO: Wh-what?

MOTHER: Wake up! You must have gone to sleep and rolled off the sofa.

NANCY JO: [*sitting up*] Oh Mother! [*Picks up a book and opens it and reads a couple of lines*] It isn't true! I can read! I can read! Oh, Mother! Is that awful Raven gone?

MOTHER: [*puzzled*] Raven? What on earth are you talking about, dear?

NANCY JO: Oh, Mother. I had the awfullest nightmare! Those old Witches and Hamlet, and the Three Musketeers, and that awful Raven! [*Shivers*] Oh, it was terrible! They said I never could read anymore. Oh Mother! I just *love* to read! I couldn't live without reading could I, Mother?

231

MOTHER: [*getting up*] I expect not. But it was only a
dream. Come now, dear. Supper is ready. [*Starts out*]

NANCY JO: [*hugging her book*] Oh, book, I just love you!
I can't wait to read you. Am I glad I can read!

[CURTAIN]

An Hour at the Library

Written and presented by the Fourth Grade

of

Garnett School
Fairview Village, Ohio

Under the Supervision of
Ruth Bryan Beaglehole, Teacher

No royalty fee required for production

An Hour at the Library

CHARACTERS:
  BOB
  JACK
  LIBRARIAN
  READING CLUB MEMBERS

ACT I

SCENE: Street; Bob and Jack in conversation

CHARACTERS:
  BOB
  JACK

BOB: [*Enters singing to tune of "Oh, Susanna"*] Oh, I come from Coffinbury and have a great big book with me—I am going to the library, a new book for to see. Oh, Susanna—[*Meets* JACK] Oh, hello Jack, where are you going?

JACK: Hello, Bob, why I'm going skating, how about you?

BOB: I'm going to the library—today is story hour.

JACK: Well, I have a book that was due back last week but I'll let it go today.

BOB: You better not Jack—you know what that means.

JACK: No, what does it mean?

BOB: That means you can't borrow another book for three weeks.

JACK: Oh, well that wouldn't bother me much for I'm not too fond of reading anyway, and I'm not anxious about giving up my skating, but maybe I'd better take it back. There won't be many skating anyway if this is library day.

Bob: Oh, come on, take your book back and I'll go skating
with you after story hour.

Jack: Wait till I get my book.

[*Jack disappears. Bob whistles*]

Jack: [*Appears with book*] O.K., I'm ready.

Bob: [*enthusiastically*] Here we go Jack—I'm anxious to
get there today. There are going to be some new books
in the library and I want to see them. Then Miss Baker
has a surprise too. I can hardly wait to find out what
it is.

Jack: I'm not one bit anxious.

ACT II

Scene: At the library. A number of boys and girls in line at the
desk, holding books. Others about the room.

Characters:

Librarian
Bob
Jack
Reading Club members

[Librarian *is checking in and out books for many children.* Jack *and* Bob *are at the end of the line. She
greets each child with a friendly remark*]

Jack: Bob, I just can't understand you—you're sure a
good sport at all outdoor games, but still you spend
every Thursday after school down here.

Bob: You bet, there are some swell books here. Next to
baseball, I like reading best, and I think if I got started
on a good book first, even the baseball would have to
wait.

[*Jack and Bob reach the desk*]

Librarian: Hello Bob, did you like the story of the Arkansas Bear?

Bob: Yes, I think it was the best I've ever read.

236

LIBRARIAN: That's good, I have another book for you by the same author.

[*Jack comes next*]

JACK: [*shyly*] Hello, Miss Baker.

LIBRARIAN: Why hello, Jack—did you finish your book? Why Jack, what is the matter with this book? It's just about ruined.

JACK: [*stammering*] Well, er—I—you see, I got interested in a snowball fight on the way home from here and left the book out all night.

LIBRARIAN: I'm very sorry Jack, but it will be necessary for you to pay for this book.

JACK: Oh gee, that isn't fair.

LIBRARIAN: Yes, it's quite fair, Jack. You see we have definite rules about caring for books, which must be carried out.

JACK: Rules—what are they?

LIBRARIAN: Our Story Hour Club is just ready to meet, so why not join us today, Jack, and we will review the rules on how to care for books.

[*While the discussion is going on the Club Members seat themselves in a circle. Jack joins them hesitatingly*]

LIBRARIAN: Reading Group, we're going to have a visitor this afternoon. Jack Gray, I'm sure most of you know him.

[*Children greet Jack*]

LIBRARIAN: Among other things, Jack would like to learn how to care for books so let's review those rules.

SANDRA: "Always wash one's hands before handling a book."

TED: "Never mark in books."

VERA: "Never turn down the leaves of a book to mark pages."

BILLY S.: "Keep books out of reach of small children."

JOHN: "Do not bend books back."

FRANCES: "Don't wet fingers to turn pages."

FRANKLYN: "Close book when not reading it."

JIMMIE: "Return books when they are due—you can usually get a renewal."

JEAN R.: "Any book that is lost, destroyed or damaged must be paid for."

LIBRARIAN: Now Jack, you see, every one must take good care of borrowed books, even the members of the Reading Club.

JACK: My, I didn't realize there were so many things to remember about how to handle and care for books. From now on I will be much more careful.

LIBRARIAN: And now for the surprise. So many of you have read and enjoyed books by Kate Seredy that today I am going to tell you something about her life and how she became a writer.

Kate Seredy was born in Hungary. She always loved to draw so when she grew up, she drew pictures for people who wrote children's books. She was doing quite well until the depression came, and few books were bought and so few were published that there were no books for Kate to illustrate. She began to worry, for her money was very low. One Friday, on February 13th, when she was on her way out to the garage for her car as she was going to see a publisher, a beautiful big, black, shiny cat ran across her path and darted under the porch. He was a stray cat, so she didn't bother much until she returned to find him still there. He would only eat when he was left entirely alone. The publisher whom Kate Seredy had gone to see, told her to write her own books and do her own illustrating. So that very night she began the story of her own childhood, *The Good Master.* All the time she worked on this book, the black cat stayed but it would never make up. On the very day that Miss Seredy completed her book the cat disappeared and never has she seen it since. She jokingly says the cat brought her luck. Today, she has several other books: *The Singing Tree, White Stag,* and *Listening.* Maybe you have read those too. Which of you would like to tell the part of *The Good Master* you liked best?"

[*Children may select and tell part they liked best*]

SANDRA: Gypsies.

TED: Corral.

VERA: First part of story.

LIBRARIAN: Today, two boys are going to tell us something about the book they enjoyed most during this year.

NEAL: *The Little House on Wheels,* and Bud Thomas will tell us about *The Arkansas Bear.*

LIBRARIAN: [*After the boys have finished*] Well Jack, how did you enjoy our story hour?

JACK: That was great—I wish I could be a member.

LIBRARIAN: You can Jack, very easily, after you have paid for your last book. All you have to do is pledge to handle books very carefully, to read at least one book a month, and to make two oral reports a year. Of course you will want to come to story hour every week.

JACK: I know what I'll do—I'll pay for the book with my circus money, then I can come to next week's story hour.

LIBRARIAN: That will be fine. Now let's all give our pledge together.

"I will read at least one book a month.
"I will plan to give two oral reports a year.
"And above all, I will handle books carefully and try to return them just as I received them."

[CURTAIN]

Books in the Making of America
by
Lera Covington

No royalty fee required for production

SCENE 3 : No equipment
SCENE 4 : No equipment.   May take place in front of stage
             curtain
SCENE 5 : Small cherry tree and hatchet
SCENE 6 : Tree with carving on it
SCENE 7 : Same as Scene 6
SCENE 8 : Steps and two lanterns for watchman
SCENE 9 : Table and scroll.   Chair
SCENE 10 : Chair and red, white and blue bunting.
SCENE 11 : Steps may be used for Key to rest one foot on.
             Flag, drums, note pad
SCENE 12 : Stool
SCENE 13 : Pistols
SCENE 14 : Lantern
SCENE 15 : Gravel, picks and shovels
SCENE 16 : Steps
SCENE 17 : Piano or desk
SCENE 18 : In front of curtain
SCENE 19 : Bed with covering
SCENE 20 : Table with chemicals
SCENE 21 : Spy glasses
SCENE 22 : American flag

COSTUMES AND CHARACTERISTICS:

ANNOUNCER—must be a good reader and a person who can "keep the program going" when the response is weak.

FOUR QUIZ KIDS—two boys and two girls are preferable. Since they appear on the program without rehearsing four children who are alert, intelligent, and possess ability to act should be selected.

The costumes for the characters in the dramatizations should be as near like their actual dress as possible.

Since the timing for drawing the curtain for the dramatizations is very important, a responsible person should be selected for this task and should take part in the rehearsals.

Two people should be selected to set up and clear the stage.

STAGE:

The action of the book characters should take place on a small stage, set in the center of the larger stage or platform on which the play is given. The curtain should be drawn back between scenes only far enough to disclose the small stage. Before the curtain, the QUIZ KIDS should be seated in a row at one side of the platform, while the ANNOUNCER and his microphone occupy the opposite side. Behind the Announcer and near the front of the stage may be hung a large American Flag.

244

Books in the Making of America

A Radio Broadcast Featuring
The Quiz Kids

ANNOUNCER: This is [*Name of school*], [*Location of school*] operating on a frequency of 4141 bookcycles. Clifton Fadiman [*Real name of person may be substituted*] speaking. Ladies and Gentlemen, I have looked forward to this occasion for quite a long time. Since books do play such a large part on this program, we join with all book lovers throughout the land in saying "Good Books, Good Friends." [*Current book week slogan may be substituted*] All of us are thinking more of our country today than ever before. For this reason we are going to base our program on books and book characters that have helped make American history. While our guests are arriving will you please stand and sing "God Bless America"?

[*Audience sings*]

ANNOUNCER: Young people of the [*Name of school*], it gives me great pleasure to present to you those Radio Famous Quiz Kids, those intellectual pin wheels, ———, ———, ———, and ———. Now little Quizzes, how would you like to turn back the pages of American history and have a quiz in the form of "Who am I in the making of American history?"

QUIZ KIDS: [*Answer enthusiastically*]

ANNOUNCER: Remember, if you know the answer raise your hand. I shall call on the audience if you fail.

Until the early part of the 17th century America remained a country where only the red man lived. In 1607 there came to our land a small band of English people seeking freedom. This little band of people settled at Jamestown in Virginia.

[*Curtain opens. Enter* JOHN SMITH *in a struggle with two* INDIANS. *As they draw an ax to cut his head off* POCAHONTAS *runs in and saves his life by her pleadings*]

Sterling Farmer writes, "Who am I who saved this colony from the Indians?"

[*Curtain closes*]

QUIZ KIDS: [*Answer*]

ANNOUNCER: In 1620 there landed in Plymouth, Massachusetts, another group of people seeking freedom—a freedom that would allow them to worship as they pleased. These people were called Pilgrims.

[*Curtain opens.* PRISCILLA *is seated beside an old spinning wheel winding strands of yarn. Helping her is* JOHN ALDEN *who stands behind a chair with the skein around his hands*]

Mary Earthman would like for you to give the author, title and major characters in a narrative poem written about these people.

[*Curtain closes*]

QUIZ KIDS: [*Answer*]

ANNOUNCER: The first years of colonization in America were years of great suffering. Many people died of starvation. Many colonists perished, but the others did not give up.

[*Curtain opens. Enter* COLONIAL TWINS]

The Fifth Grade say that there lived at this time in a

fine brick mansion in Virginia a boy and a girl who were twins. Are you acquainted with them?

[*Curtain closes*]

Quiz Kids: [*Answer*]

Announcer: Home life in the southern colonies was quite gay. Parties were frequent occasions. Dancing was enjoyed by both old and young.

[*Curtain opens.* Five couples *of Fifth Grade children dance the Virginia Reel. Curtain closes*]

During this period was born a person who was destined to become the country's first leader.

[*Curtain opens.* George Washington *as a small boy is chopping down a cherry tree*]

Many stories are told about his honesty. The most often told is probably the cherry tree incident. The Fourth Grade would like to know the author and title of a biography written about this famous character.

[*Curtain closes*]

Quiz Kids: [*Answer*]

Announcer: The frontier of the United States is now moving toward the Mississippi. Much has been written about the brave souls who endured such hardships as they pierced through the wilderness. Helen Brogden would like for you to identify this biographical sketch.

[*Curtain opens.* Daniel Boone *is carving on a tree*]

I am America's most famous pioneer. My trails extend through North Carolina, Tennessee, Kentucky and Virginia. In 1767 I made my first expedition into the wilds of Kentucky. During my travels I experienced many attacks by the Indians. There is a fort on the Kentucky River which bears my name. Who am I?

Quiz Kids: [*Answer*]

247

ANNOUNCER: Men were not the only ones who loved adventure. Margaret Buchanan describes here another pioneer.

[BECKY LANDERS *comes in and starts talking with Daniel Boone*]

I am a very brave girl. I live in Kentucky and am a very good friend of Daniel Boone's. I had many adventures with the Indians. My father was killed by them and my brother was held captive. Who am I?

[*Curtain closes*]

QUIZ KIDS: [*Answer*]

ANNOUNCER: By the middle of the 18th century the colonists were growing tired of being governed by England. Wars had left the mother country deeply in debt and she began to tax the colonists. They refused to be taxed saying that this was taxation without representation. War between the colonies and England soon broke out. Joan Yearwood would like to know what character is talking here and who is the author of the poem.

[*Curtain opens.* WATCHMAN *enters with two lanterns, walks back and forth, then climbs to hang both lanterns*]

"If the British march
By land or sea from the town tonight,
Hang a lantern aloft in the belfry arch
Of the North Church tower as a signal light,—
One, if by land, and two, if by sea;
And I on the opposite shore will be, . . . "

[*Curtain closes*]

QUIZ KIDS: [*Answer*]

ANNOUNCER: In the following year, on July 4, 1776, was written one of the most important documents in American history.

[*Curtain opens.* THOMAS JEFFERSON *is seated by a desk writing on a document*]

Agnes Mae Jackson would like to know what this document was, and the number of people who signed it.

[*Curtain closes*]

QUIZ KIDS: [*Answer*]

ANNOUNCER: Every country has its flag. The colonies are now thirteen in number and have declared themselves independent of the mother country.

[*Curtain opens.* BETSY ROSS *is sewing on red, white and blue bunting*]
Legend tells that an obscure seamstress of Philadelphia was sitting in her home on Arch Street when she was visited by a delegation from Congress headed by George Washington. This committee asked her to make the first flag of the United States. Gertrude Sanders wishes to know who this person was.

[*Curtain closes*]

QUIZ KIDS: [*Answer*]

ANNOUNCER: By 1787 our Constitution was written, and in 1789 George Washington was elected the first President of the United States. In 1803 the Louisiana Purchase was made. America was expanding rapidly, but by 1812 another war was raging. The British were interfering with American trade; American sailors were taken from American ships. Again the states take a stand against the mother country.

[*Curtain opens.* FRANCIS SCOTT KEY *stands writing on a note pad and watching the American flag wave off side of stage. Roars of cannon and guns are heard off stage*]
Engaged in the battle of Fort McHenry was a young lawyer. It looked as if the fort would be burned, but over the ramparts the American flag still waved. Stand-

249

ing there watching the flag as it stood amid the flame this young man took a note pad from his pocket and wrote our national anthem. [*Curtain closes*] "Who was this young lawyer?" asks Thomas White.

QUIZ KIDS: [*Answer*]

ANNOUNCER: Edward Everett Hale has written a book that it would be well for every American citizen to read. Jack Evans would like for the Quiz Kids to identify this person.

[*Curtain opens.* PHILIP NOLAN *is seen first stamping his foot in an act of blaspheming the United States. He then drops to a stool in great remorse*]

I once became involved with Aaron Burr in an act of treason against the United States. At a trial in Virginia in a fit of frenzy I blasphemed the United States and expressed the wish never to hear of my country again. The court punished me by seeing that this terrible wish was granted. For nearly fifty years I lived on the sea never hearing the name of my country mentioned. I loved my country as no other man has loved her, yet I am known as "The Man Without a Country."

[*Curtain closes*]

QUIZ KIDS: [*Answer*]

ANNOUNCER: In this same war of 1812, writes Matt Hodgson, there was a general who directed the forces in the Battle of New Orleans. He liked to fight and engaged in many duels. Who was this general and what great position did he later fill?

[*Curtain opens.* JACKSON *and* DICKINSON *are seen with backs to each other. As the referee counts three they turn and advance three steps. Jackson opens his coat as he steps. They shoot. Jackson staggers. Quick curtain*]

QUIZ KIDS: [*Answer*]

250

ANNOUNCER: By the middle of the 19th century pioneers were braving the wilderness and moving rapidly toward the Pacific. Hilda White would like for you to identify one of this group.

[*Curtain opens.* ABBIE DEAL *from "A Lantern in her Hand" stands holding lantern uplifted in one hand*]

I was born in a log cabin in Iowa during pioneer days. From there I moved to Nebraska where I reared my family with all the courage of a pioneer mother. With a lantern in my hand I had gone forth to light the way for future generations. I died alone in a pioneer home, surrounded by the memories of a long full life.

[*Curtain closes*]

QUIZ KIDS: [*Answer*]

ANNOUNCER: In 1848 news spread of the discovery of gold in California. Many stories were told of these adventures.

[*Curtain opens.* GOLD DIGGERS *with shovels and picks are seen picking up gravel and examining it*]

Marjorie McFolin says that Steward Edward White has written a novel which gives a very vivid description of how this precious metal was found and of the hardships these people underwent on their trail across the continent. What is my title?

[*Curtain closes*]

QUIZ KIDS: [*Answer*]

ANNOUNCER: Much has been written about the Civil War. Margaret Miller has selected here her favorite character.

[*Curtain opens.* ANN RUTLEDGE *is seated on top of steps.* ABRAHAM LINCOLN *stands at bottom holding her hand*]

251

I lived during the early part of the 19th century. My home was in a little town named New Salem in the State of Illinois. I was the childhood sweetheart of Abraham Lincoln. I died while in my youth. Who am I?

[*Curtain closes*]

Quiz Kids: [*Answer*]

Announcer: After the Civil War came a period of Reconstruction. Terrible conditions prevailed in the Southern States. State governments were corrupt and leaders were dishonest. In spite of all this suffering the people could still sing. Most popular of the songs they sang were those written by the man described here by Susan Waller.

[*Curtain opens.* STEPHEN FOSTER *is seated either at desk or at piano writing or playing softly one of his songs*]
I am a native of Pennsylvania. I cared little for fame or money but I could not escape popularity which seems to be growing with the 20th century. I had no formal training in music, yet I composed over a hundred songs. Nearly a fourth of them are Negro melodies, and the remainder are sentimental ballads. Who am I?

[*Curtain closes*]

Quiz Kids: [*Answer*]

Announcer: What could be a greater treat at this time than to have four belles of Stephen Foster's day sing one of his favorites, "Jeannie with the Light Brown Hair"?

[FOUR GIRLS *sing in front of curtain while stage is being set for next scene*]

Far greater than any general who fought in the Spanish American War was the social worker described here by Marie Jackson.

252

[*Curtain opens.* CLARA BARTON *is seated at the bedside of a sick person*]

I was born in 1821 at Oxford, Massachusetts. I became deeply interested in soldiers' relief work during the War of Secession. I named and marked the graves of over 12,000 soldiers in the Andersonville National Cemetery. In 1873 I organized the first branch of the American Red Cross. During the Spanish American War I took charge in the yellow fever epidemic. Who am I?

[*Curtain closes*]

QUIZ KIDS: [*Answer*]

ANNOUNCER: Following the period of Reconstruction the increased use of machinery brought about great changes in our ways of working and living. Because of the many inventions and improvements our country has advanced so rapidly that no nation in the history of the world has made so much progress over an equal period of time. No person had a greater part in this progress than the man described here by Thomas Huddleston.

[*Curtain opens.* THOMAS ALVA EDISON *is seated working by a table on which are various chemicals*]

I was born in Milan, Ohio in 1847. I spent only three months of my life in school. The teachers thought I was a dunce. I was a wide reader and my favorite study was chemistry. To earn pocket money to stock my laboratory, I got a job as train boy, but I set the baggage car on fire with chemicals and was thrown off. For my many inventions and discoveries I earned the name of "America's Wizard of Invention." Who am I?

[*Curtain closes*]

QUIZ KIDS: [*Answer*]

ANNOUNCER: Nations do not stay at peace long. In 1914 there broke out in Europe the First World War. The destruction, cost and misery of all the wars of a thousand years did not equal this terrible conflict. On April 6, 1917 our country became engaged in this horrible war. Representative of the American boys who went over sea is the description sent in by Jean Buckner, who would like you to name the author and title of the book from which this character is taken.

[*Curtain opens.* Boy, *from "Falcons of France" by Nordhoff and Hall, dressed in air pilot's clothes, looks through spy glasses as if watching for planes overhead*]

I was eager to enter the war and volunteered along with my friend, Seldon, to join the Lafayette Flying Corps. At first it was great adventure and I liked it, but it didn't take me long to grow tired of it. War is horrible.

[*Curtain closes*]

Quiz Kids: [*Answer*]

Announcer: Time marches on. In this year of 1941 Democracy is on trial. Every day important history is being written. Our forefathers have founded for us a great country; it is our duty as American citizens to love it and to defend it.

[*Curtain opens.* Five Girl *and* five Boy Scouts *stand in semicircle, facing the American flag*]

The Girl and Boy Scout organizations which have become very active since the World War will close our program by leading the audience first in giving the pledge to our flag and then in singing "The Star Spangled Banner."

[Curtain]

At Your Service

by

Martha R. Eckert and Ellen Kroll

No royalty fee required for production

At Your Service

A Radio Play

This play was written for and presented on the High School Workshop Hour, a weekly radio broadcast for the Indianapolis Public Schools.

With a few modifications, it can be presented equally well as a stage play. For the latter use a radio broadcasting studio as the setting. The only equipment needed is a microphone, chairs, and signs, either printed or electric, "On the Air," and "Stand By." The Station Announcer may introduce the program by saying:

"We welcome you as our radio audience for today's broadcast of 'At Your Service,' a radio play in one act. We hope you will enjoy the play and applaud as directed." (The Announcer should be a jovial person who can get the audience to laugh at the occasional puns, and applaud at the end. If desired, he may announce the characters at the beginning or end.)

CHARACTERS:

STATION ANNOUNCER
STUDENT ANNOUNCER
1st BOOKWORM
2nd BOOKWORM
ELLEN ⎫
CARLA ⎬ Students
MADGE ⎭

[MUSIC—*Record of School Song*]

STATION ANNOUNCER: The High School Workshop! Presented this afternoon by students from ——————— High School, and announced by ———————.

STUDENT ANNOUNCER: One morning before school has started we find two bookworms munching their way through the atlas in the ——————— Library. The first bookworm is speaking to his friend.

1st Bookworm: We're lucky to find this nice atlas for breakfast. Most of the books are used so often around here that I can't get a good meal.

2nd Bookworm: Quite right, Brother Worm. The other day I was starting through a history book when a bright senior opened it and—

1st Bookworm: Well, did that give you a shock?

2nd Bookworm: Did it? I haven't been the same since.

1st Bookworm: Time was when we could settle down with a history of England and feel that the world was safe.

2nd Bookworm: Ah—those were the days. The books never were taken off the shelves except for dusting.

1st Bookworm: Yes, I remember going through an entire set of *Nations of the World* without being once disturbed.

2nd Bookworm: These school libraries are used so much now that I can't even get a square meal.

1st Bookworm: You do look like skin and bones, brother. I can almost count your vertebrae!

2nd Bookworm: If those food books weren't used so often I might get a chance at some vitamins.

1st Bookworm: I tried that stunt too, but one day I got into the math books by mistake, and did I have indigestion!

2nd Bookworm: I can't recommend a good meal anymore since every department uses this library.

1st Bookworm: Those social studies pupils surely keep me on the jump!

2nd Bookworm: And the English students, too. I didn't think anyone read Burns' poetry, and had just settled down for a nap when a student woke me up in a hurry. I heard her say she was looking for a "Field Mouse" or something like that.

1st Bookworm: I even tried changing my address to the Vertical File, but it's no use. Those students are into everything.

[Sound—*Bell ringing*]

2nd Bookworm: There's the bell, so we'd better get into the atlas before the students come.

1st Bookworm: Good idea. I'll take South America and you try Asia. Stay away from Europe, though; it is already fairly well chewed up.

Ellen: Oh hello, Carla, are you coming to the Library Club meeting this afternoon?

Carla: Yes, I had such a good time at the last meeting that I wouldn't miss this one for anything. Wasn't the book review of *I Married Adventure* the most thrilling account you ever heard?

Ellen: It certainly was! Now that we have the book in the library, I can hardly wait to read it. By the way, have you finished your workbook?

Carla: Only two more exercises, and it really has taught me about the library. Since I'm going to be a librarian, I'm eager to get all the experience I can. Working here should help me in college, and also in applying for a position this summer.

Ellen: I don't suppose I'll be a librarian. I wasn't sure what I did want to be until last semester. We had to write a vocational theme for English, and the teacher said that there were pamphlets on almost every kind of job in the library. I looked through them and decided to write about secretarial work. I just found out that my experience in working here will help me in case I want to do filing.

Carla: We certainly do get plenty of experience in that. Every day more cards have to be alphabetized and filed in the card catalog.

259

ELLEN: I like the job of taking care of the Vertical File. The vocational pamphlets are there, and other pamphlets on hundreds of different subjects. Just last week some pictures were donated to the library, and it was fun putting them in their proper places.

CARLA: I'll never forget the time an art student asked me for a picture of an Indian snake charmer. Luckily I found one in the Vertical File.

ELLEN: Oh, look, Carla, here comes Madge.

CARLA: Hello, Madge, how are you?

MADGE: Well, I would feel much better if the debate we're having in speech class was over. We'll never win unless we can find more material for the Negative side, and I happen to be on it.

CARLA: Didn't you get any books from the library?

MADGE: Oh, yes, but we need more recent facts.

ELLEN: Well, have you tried the *Readers' Guide*?

MADGE: That's a thought. I do remember something about the *Readers' Guide* from our library lessons; an index to magazine articles, isn't it?

CARLA: Of course. You can find enough material in our library to win that debate. You might even try Ellen's pet information bureau, the Vertical File.

MADGE: You two certainly know lots about the library. Do you really like to work at the desk?

CARLA: Oh, yes, it's loads of fun; something interesting happens every day.

ELLEN: Interesting and amusing, I would say. Yesterday when I was charging books, a girl asked me if we had anything about a common cold. I told her we couldn't fill any prescriptions, but we could certainly give her some ideas.

CARLA: Ideas make the world go round, and I imagine lots of them came from libraries.

260

ELLEN: I'll never forget the time a student asked me for the pink canoe. After I had looked all over the library she still insisted that we had something about a red boat!

MADGE: Imagine wanting something about a red boat.

ELLEN: That's just what I did—imagine—and finally it dawned on me that she wanted the "Rubaiyat."

MADGE: Oh, you mean the poem, "The Rubaiyat," by Omar Khayyam?

ELLEN: Yes. And another student asked me one day to find something about "pasture." I looked everywhere, under pasture, meadow, and field, and had about given up, when the student said, "You might look under Louis; it's his first name."

CARLA: Louis Pasteur, of course. I bet you counted to ten, and then some.

ELLEN: I certainly did, but "Live and learn" is my motto since I started to be a student library assistant.

MADGE: It sounds as though you never have a dull moment in the library. I wouldn't mind being a student assistant if I could read all the new books.

CARLA: Oh, have you seen the ones that the English classes bought for the library? Our class gave two, *The Tree of Liberty,* by Elizabeth Page, and *Three's a Crew,* by Kathrene Pinkerton. These are both popular books of the year, and I'm anxious to read them.

ELLEN: Our class chose some vocational fiction since we had to write those essays. We bought *Betty Blake,* by Stern, and *Sue Barton,* by Boylston. Both are about nursing, only *Betty Blake* is an occupational-therapist and Sue Barton is a superintendent of nurses.

MADGE: I just finished Jeanette Nolan's new book, *The Gay Poet,* which our class gave. Eugene Field had so many humorous adventures that the book hardly seemed like biography. I sat down with it one evening and

261

laughed all the way through. It has the cleverest illustrations!

CARLA: That reminds me. Do you know who is on the poster committee for this month besides you and me?

ELLEN: No, I'm not sure, but the names are on the bulletin board in the library work room. I hope we are on the committee for Book Week,—it's so much fun to decorate the show case and make posters.

MADGE: I'm almost sold on the idea of belonging to the Library Club from hearing you two talk about it. What are my chances of becoming a member?

ELLEN: You have to have a good grade and be interested in the work, but I know that you would be accepted.

MADGE: If the library can help me win that debate, I'll be an ardent member of the club. I'll start right now with the *Readers' Guide*.

ELLEN: Luck to you, and don't forget to use my pet, the Vertical File.

CARLA: Don't get lost in it either. We are still counting on you for the Library Club. So long.

ELLEN: Now that just shows how important the library really is. It has all the answers as far as my grades are concerned.

CARLA: Grades, and other things as well. I had to introduce my date to several couples at the last school dance, and I was certainly glad I had already read those etiquette books. Emily Post couldn't have made a better introduction herself, and Ted even complimented me for being so at ease socially.

ELLEN: Boys seem to be more conscious of such things now. Barbour's book of *Good Manners for Boys* seems to be as popular as *Smoky the Cowhorse*.

CARLA: Speaking of cows, that reminds me of the meat charts I'm supposed to find for one of the students. Just before the bell rang yesterday, a boy asked me if I could tell him how to carve a cow.

ELLEN: Evidently he is going to be a butcher and is having my experience with a vocational essay.

CARLA: I suppose so. I hope there is something in the card catalog on the subject.

ELLEN: You might look under butchering or meat, and I believe we have some charts in the file. There's no end to these questions about cows! One student asked me for the population of Moscow, but I soon answered that by using the *World Almanac*.

CARLA: That is a good reference book for figures, but I don't believe it has the figure of a cow. I'll look in the catalog right away.

ELLEN: In the meantime, I'll be returning these reserve books to the shelves.

CARLA: [*slight pause*] Butchering—see Meat. Oh, that means that everything in the library on butchering is under the heading, Meat. Mary—Masefield—Meat—ah, here it is. Bailey, Edgar, *Food Products,* pages 341 to 366, call number 641-B. There should be some meat charts in that book. Now for the Vertical File. Why, imagine finding you here, Madge. Are you getting any materials?

MADGE: Materials? I am going to have enough information to answer any statement the Affirmative gives. All I have to do now is to read the magazine articles that I found listed in the *Readers' Guide.*

CARLA: Go to the desk, then, and Ellen will get the magazines out of the stacks. All the past issues are in the store room.

MADGE: I am certainly learning my way around here; I suppose I should have taken those library lessons more seriously, but I had no idea that there was so much to be gained from knowing how to find things.

CARLA: As I said before, the library is the best place in the whole school, always at your service! Oh, it is almost time for the next class.

[SOUND—*Bell*]

CARLA: There's the bell now. I'll see you at the club meeting this afternoon.

[*Fade out—*]

STUDENT ANNOUNCER: We leave the three students and return to our friends, the bookworms.

1ST BOOKWORM: You spoke of a long, varied career. What do you mean?

2ND BOOKWORM: In my time I have been through the best books in this library. I know well the works of Dickens, Thackeray, and Longfellow, not to mention Shelley, Keats, and Browning.

1ST BOOKWORM: I, too, have digested the works of the masters, but I like better the works of the newer, younger writers. Their books serve as inspiration and guidance to the millions of young people who read them. I feel that the works of the masters are all very well, but they serve mostly now only as good examples.

2ND BOOKWORM: I would challenge you to an argument on that question if I were not so full of South America. As it is, I am far too sleepy to bother. Ho-hum. [*Yawn*]

1ST BOOKWORM: Quiet! I hear somebody coming. Let's get out of this atlas.

2ND BOOKWORM: They must even use *it* around here, though I'm sure I don't know what good it will do, the way the world is being changed lately.

1ST BOOKWORM: This is the last straw! I have a friend who lives in a research library, and he says that he usually can find a nice volume that isn't used every day. We'll visit him until this library isn't busy.

2ND BOOKWORM : Personally, I don't think that this library will ever *not* be busy. Hurry up! Let's hide behind the radiator until we can make our getaway. Slide under this pipe, Brother Worm!

[CURTAIN]